MODEL STEAM
LOCOMOTIVES

The Author

The **15-in. gauge Pacific type locomotive "GREEN GODDESS"** designed by the author and built by Messrs. Davey, Paxman and Co. Ltd., Colchester, for the **Romney, Hythe and Dymchurch Railway, Kent.** The locomotive is shown with its designer at Ravenglass, Cumberland, undergoing trials on the **Ravenglass and Eskdale Railway** prior to being placed in regular passenger service on the R.H. & D.R.

Principal Dimensions: Length 24′ 9″   Width 3′ 1″
Height 4′ 7″
Boiler Pressure 180 lb. sq. in.
Tractive Effort 1,470 lb.
Adhesive Weight 6,600 lb.
Total Weight in Working Order 7¾ tons.

MODEL STEAM LOCOMOTIVES

by HENRY GREENLY

REVISED BY

ERNEST A. STEEL
Assoc.I.Mech.E., M.J.I.Engrs.

He who is theoretic as well as practical is therefore doubly armed; able to prove the propriety of his designs, but equally so to carry them into execution

VITRUVIUS

© The Estates of Henry Greenly & Ernest A. Steel 2005

First edition	*1922*
Seventh edition (completely revised)	*1951*
Eighth edition	*1954*

All the above published by Cassell & Company Limited

This printing 2005

British Library Cataloguing-in-Publication-Data:
a catalogue record of this book is held by the British Library.

ISBN No. 0-9547131-2-5

Published in Great Britain by:
CAMDEN MINIATURE STEAM SERVICES
Barrow Farm, Rode, Frome, Somerset. BA11 6PS U.K.
www.camdenmin.co.uk

Camden stock one of the widest selections of model engineering, technical and transportation books to be found.
Contact them at the above address for a copy of their latest free Booklist.

Printed and bound by Biddles Ltd., Kings Lynn.

PLEASE NOTE!
In this book, the authors and publisher are only passing on knowledge, some of which may have been overtaken by the march of time and technology. Your safety, and that of others, is your responsibility, both in the workshop and when running any locomotive in your care.

PREFACE TO SEVENTH EDITION

THE first edition of this book appeared in 1922 and since then five other editions have been published; the last in 1937. Thus during a period of nearly a quarter of a century, *Model Steam Locomotives* has served as a standard text-book for model engineers and amateurs throughout the English-speaking world.

The late Henry Greenly began his professional career in connection with locomotive engineering about 1899–1900. His first 15 in. gauge locomotive, the famous LITTLE GIANT, was an Atlantic type built in 1904 by Messrs. Bassett-Lowke, Ltd. It was indeed the pioneer of British miniature railway engines to be followed a few years later by the equally famous SANS PARIEL. This latter locomotive saw considerable service on the Ravenglass and Eskdale Railway, Cumberland. The "Pacific" type locomotive, COLOSSUS, was contemporary with the famous GREAT BEAR of the G.W.R.—these two engines being the only "Pacifics" employed in this country at the period prior to 1920. In 1924 Mr. Greenly designed his one-third scale "Pacifics" for the Romney, Hythe and Dymchurch Railway, Kent.

But the author's interests were not solely confined to the design of locomotives for the large gauges—which also included full-size engines. His inherent capacity for locomotive design was always in evidence whether the gauge be $1\frac{1}{4}$ in. or any other of the accepted standards up to 12 in. The author states in an earlier edition that "In writing the present work, which aims at presenting a comprehensive survey of the whole subject, it has been possible to illustrate numerous types of locomotives by reproduced photographs of actual models—most of these models have been amateur made." The same objective has been the aim of the writer of this preface. It has been deemed necessary, however, to revise a considerable amount of the material in the old edition in order to bring the book up to date and to conform with modern practice. Some years ago Mr. Greenly had planned to make various alterations and additions, but the intervention of another war and his subsequent ill-health made the project impossible.

The writer had collaborated with his father-in-law in the preparation of some of the material for this edition and has since included entirely new material, particularly with reference to piston-valve cylinders. He has to thank all those model engineers, firms and British Railways (Western Region) who have loaned photographs and drawings for publication; to Mrs. H. Greenly for permission to examine books and records. He is also greatly indebted to his wife, Elenora Howard for the preparation of all the new line drawings and for her helpful suggestions and criticisms in the preparation of this work. Finally, credit must be given to his son John for compiling the nomograph.

ERNEST A. STEEL

PREFACE TO EIGHTH EDITION

THE continued demand for *Model Steam Locomotives* since its publication in revised form in 1951 has necessitated the issue of this further edition, and the opportunity has been taken to bring it up to date with new drawings and additional information, and to correct a number of errors overlooked in the last edition. In this connection, correspondents at home and abroad are thanked for their valued communications.

The full-size steam locomotive continues to hold its position on railways of all gauges in the face of other forms of traction and its popularity is reflected in the ever-increasing number of model railways that are being constructed for steam traction from $1\frac{1}{4}$ in. to 15 in. gauge. Fundamentally, the steam locomotive is the same to-day as its prototype of a century ago: in fact, all that is demanded is an efficient boiler, a well-designed engine and valve gear and efficient handling on the road—the *sine qua non* of the model steam locomotive too.

In order to assist the model engineer to select a scale-model steam locomotive for construction in his own workshop, a companion volume under the title of *Greenly's Model Steam Locomotive Designs and Specifications* has been prepared for "Cassell's New Model Maker Series" (Price 4s. 6d.). Therein will be found numerous locomotive designs in various gauges based on the principles discussed in the following pages.

ERNEST A. STEEL

CONTENTS

LIST OF TABLES

CHAPTER I

CHOICE OF SCALE AND GAUGE

Introduction

THE model locomotive is the most popular of all working miniatures. This is due to the interest displayed in the locomotive itself, and also to the fact that this type of prime mover is self contained; it includes the machinery for converting the heat of the fuel into useful work and carries with it the necessary generator, fuel and water.

Model engineers approach the construction of a model locomotive from different points of view. Some do not look to the completion and running of the engine so much as to the pleasure that will be derived from the making and assembling of the parts and in the appearance of the finished machine. Others prefer to see a model locomotive at work. As in real practice, the labour of construction should be a means to an end. Endeavour should be made to obtain the maximum power on the given gauge, and there is no need to follow any particular prototype, so long as the exterior design is one which would be reasonable in real practice.

The beginner in model locomotive work should not be too ambitious. In preference to selecting at the outset an elaborate design, he should adopt one of a simple nature.

The history of the working model locomotive, as it is now understood, would be difficult to trace. No doubt ever since the inception of the steam locomotive, models have been made and treasured. Among miniature locomotives of note made in the early days of the "iron road" there are but few successful examples.

Scale replicas can be made to serve historical purposes, and are made either in full or partly in section. Museums and private collections all over the world contain large numbers of models. These models are, however, not within the scope of this work. They are usually made without any regard to cost by skilled workmen from the working drawings of the original.

B   [1]

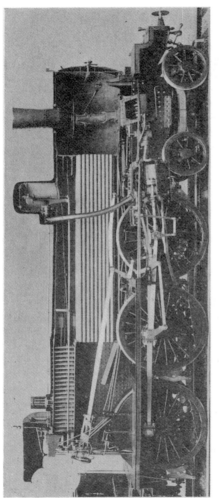

Fig. 1.—An Exhibition Model in Section of a Four-Cylinder de Glehn Compound (1901)
[Science Museum, London]

(*Photo: Courtesy of British Railways, Western Region*)

Fig. 2.—Model of "King George V" in 7¼ gauge on exhibition at Paddington Station, London. Built by Mr. B. R. Hunt, Johannesburg, S.A. and presented in 1947 to the directors of the G.W.R.

(Photo: Norman K. Sandley, Jamesville, Wisconsin, U.S.A.)

Fig. 3.—15-in. Gauge American "Hudson" Locomotive.
[Oil-fired, Return-tube Scotch Boiler]

The Choice of Scale and Gauge

The sizes of the model locomotives with which it is proposed to deal in this book will to a certain extent be limited to those built for pleasure. The larger sizes are of such proportions as to render the finished machines capable of really useful work for exhibitions, pleasure parks and estate purposes.

For example, in 1926 the Romney, Hythe and Dymchurch Railway was built to a gauge of 15 in. Later, the line was extended to Dungeness thus making it the longest public miniature railway in the world. The locomotive stock consists of various types designed by the author and modelled after famous British and Canadian prototypes. The locomotives are capable of hauling 25 passenger coaches at 30 miles per hour. The engines and tenders together total 25 ft. in length and are fitted with automatic brakes.

(Photo: "The Locomotive")

Fig. 4.—15-in. Gauge "Pacific" Locomotive "Dr. Syn". Built by
The Yorkshire Engine Co Ltd, for Romney, Hythe and Dymchurch
Railway, Kent

[3]

(Photo: H. Greenly)

Fig. 5.—0–4–0 tank locomotive, 15-in. gauge. Employed at Eskdale about 1923, it was one of the smallest "not-to-scale" working locomotives then in existence.

(Photo: J. R. Jeffress Esq.)

Fig. 6.—American 4–8–4 locomotive 7¼-in. gauge. railway.

[4]

The 10¼ in. gauge is employed for passenger carrying railways in pleasure parks and private estates. It has distinct advantages in so far as comparatively more comfort is allowed the passenger and particularly the driver. For this reason the gauge may be considered the smallest size permissible in cases where the line is used regularly for passenger-carrying purposes. The 9½ in. gauge is comparable with the 10¼ in. in this respect, and is widely employed in this country.

One of the first true-to-scale models to be employed on a 10¼ in. gauge railway was the "Royal Scot" built to the designs of the author by Messrs. Bassett-Lowke, Ltd., Engineers, Northampton, for the Marquis of Downshire.

The 9½ in. gauge engine is the largest size recommended for amateur construction. The gauge is a safe one, and engines of this size are easy to handle. Speeds up to 15 miles an hour can be obtained without trouble on a well-laid track.

Where the curves must be reduced to below 50 ft. radius a 1½-in. scale locomotive must, under ordinary circumstances, be adopted. The standard gauge for this scale is 7¼ in., and many highly successful engines of all types have been built to run on it.

The other popular gauges in general use are the 3½ and 5 in. and many successful models have been constructed to haul the driver and several passengers in both these gauges.

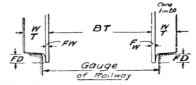

Fig. 7.—Wheel and Tyre dimensions. (See Table II.)

A practical model steam locomotive can be made to suit the popular "No. 1" or 1¾ in. gauge, but the smallest size usually recommended is the 2½ in. gauge. The prototype selected for the latter gauge should provide a boiler of ample capacity and the diameter should not be less than 3 in. The relative sizes of standard-gauge working models are shown in Fig. 3.

The various gauges are standardized and Table I provides useful and important particulars for each size. The diagram, Fig. 7, is a key to the standard wheel and tyre dimensions which are now established.

For No. 0 and No. 1 gauges much finer standard dimensions are now advocated to take the place of the so-called "coarse" standards that have been established for over twenty-five

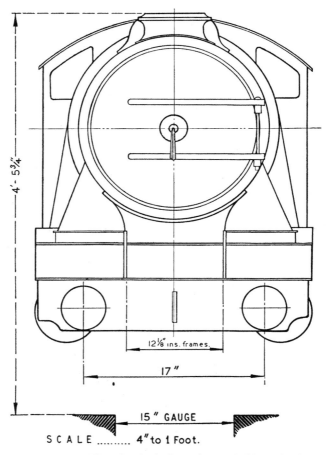

4' - 5¾"

12⅛" ins. frames.

17 "

15 " GAUGE

S C A L E .... 4" to 1 Foot.

Fig. 8.—Relative sizes of "Standard-gauge"

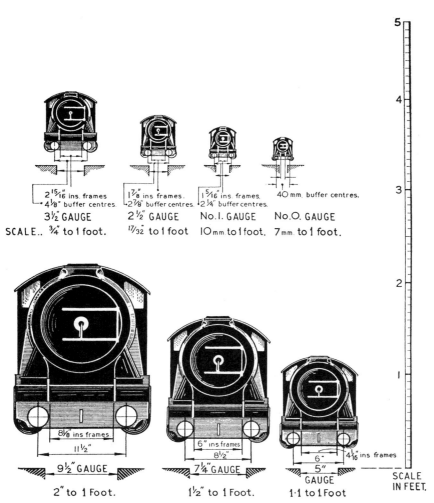

2 15/16 ins. frames
4 1/8" buffer centres.
3 1/2" GAUGE
SCALE.. 3/4" to 1 foot.

1 7/8 ins frames.
2 7/8" buffer centres.
2 1/2" GAUGE
17/32" to 1 foot

1 5/16" ins. frames.
2 1/4" buffer centres.
No. I. GAUGE
10 mm. to 1 foot.

40 mm. buffer centres.
No. O. GAUGE
7 mm. to 1 foot.

8 1/8" ins frames
11 1/2"
9 1/2" GAUGE
2" to 1 Foot.

6" ins frames
8 1/2"
7 1/4" GAUGE
1 1/2" to 1 Foot.

6"
5"
GAUGE
1·1 to 1 Foot

4 1/16" ins frames

SCALE
IN FEET.

5

4

3

2

1

Working Models from 1¼-in. to 15-in. Gauge.

[7]

TABLE I. SCALE AND GAUGE STANDARDS

Gauge inches	Scale	Radius of Curve		Average Speed m.p.h.	Average Weights		Boiler	Fuel	Standard 'British' Loading Gauge
		Min.	Average		Loco.	Loaded Train			
		ft. in.	ft. in.		lb.	lb.			
$1\frac{1}{4}$	7 mm.	3 6	6 6	2	12	—	Plain	Spirit	68 × 95 mm.
$1\frac{3}{4}$	10 mm.	4 0	9 0	3	18	—	Water tube	Charcoal	90 × 135 mm.
2	$\frac{7}{16}$ in.	4 6	10 0	4	25	—	" "	"	99 × 149 mm.
$2\frac{1}{2}$	$\frac{17}{32}$ in.	5 0	12 6	5	50	200	Loco	Coal	$4\frac{3}{4}$ in. × $7\frac{1}{4}$ in.
$3\frac{1}{4}$	$\frac{11}{16}$ in.	12 0	20 0	6	80	600	"	"	$6\frac{1}{4}$ in. × $9\frac{1}{4}$ in.
$3\frac{1}{2}$	$\frac{3}{4}$ in.	15 0	25 0	7	100	$\frac{1}{2}$ ton	"	"	$6\frac{3}{4}$ in. × $10\frac{1}{8}$ in.
$4\frac{13}{16}$	1 in.	20 0	32 0	9	2 cwt.	$\frac{1}{2}$ ton	"	"	$9\frac{1}{8}$ in. × $13\frac{1}{2}$ in.
5	$1\frac{1}{16}$ in.	25 0	35 0	10	$2\frac{1}{2}$ cwt.	$\frac{3}{4}$ ton	"	"	$9\frac{5}{8}$ in. × $14\frac{1}{4}$ in.
5	$1\frac{1}{10}$ in.	30 0	40 0	10	3 cwt.	1 ton	"	"	10 in. × $14\frac{3}{4}$ in.
$7\frac{1}{4}$	$1\frac{1}{2}$ in.	35 0	60 0	12	5 cwt.	2 ton	"	"	$13\frac{1}{2}$ in. × $20\frac{1}{4}$ in.
$9\frac{1}{2}$	2 in.	60 0	120 0	15	8 cwt.	$3\frac{1}{2}$ ton	"	"	$18\frac{1}{4}$ in. × 26 in.
$10\frac{1}{4}$	$2\frac{1}{4}$ in.	85 0	160 0	18	15 cwt.	4 ton	"	"	$20\frac{1}{2}$ in. × $29\frac{1}{4}$ in.
15	3 in.	150 0	350 0	25	2 ton	10 ton	"	"	27 in. × $40\frac{1}{2}$ in.
15	$3\frac{1}{4}$ in.	170 0	400 0	25	3 ton	15 ton	"	"	30 in. × 44 in.
15	4 in.	200 0	500 0	25	5 ton	25 ton	"	"	37 in. × $53\frac{3}{4}$ in.

Curves.—The minimum radius may be used for points, sidings and curves on slow-speed lines; for fast running use the average radius as the minimum.

Loading Gauge.—Where the American loading gauge is desired, use a scale equivalent of 10 ft. wide × 15 ft.

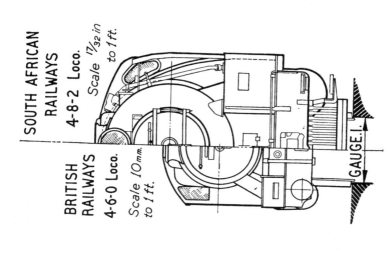

SOUTH AFRICAN RAILWAYS 4-8-2 Loco. Scale 17/32 in to 1 ft.

BRITISH RAILWAYS 4-6-0 Loco. Scale 10mm. to 1ft.

GAUGE. I.

Fig. 10.—Comparison of Two No. 1 Gauge Models. One half drawn to represent a 3 ft. 6 in. gauge locomotive in half-inch scale and the other a standard-gauge locomotive in 10 mm. scale.

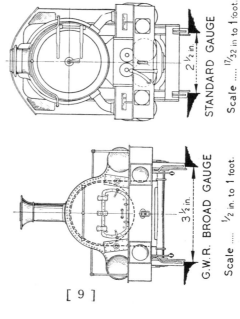

STANDARD GAUGE

Scale ..... 17/32 in to 1 foot.

2½ in.

G.W.R. BROAD GAUGE

Scale ..... ½ in. to 1 foot.

3½ in.

Fig. 9.—Comparison between a Modern "Standard" Gauge Locomotive and a G.W.R. Broad Gauge Engine of 1863 to approximately the same scale.

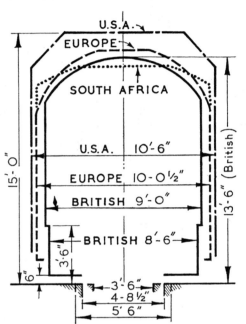

Fig. 11.—Loading Gauges of Various Countries.

years. The new standards have been drawn up by the British Railway Model Standards Bureau and include recommendations for rail sections, track and wheels. The degree of fineness recommended approaches that of dead true-to-scale but some model engineers have compromised between the old and the new standards.

Many model locomotive builders increase the loading gauge (see Figs. 10 and 11) to that of the American and Continental dimensions. There is no objection to this where the engines are modelled on "free-lance" lines. Another method of obtaining a large engine on a given gauge is to adopt the standard 3 ft. 6 in. gauge, which has a loading gauge of 12 ft. 10 in. high by 8 ft. 9 in. wide and scale down accordingly.

Where it is desired to build an engine of the smallest possible size to haul passengers, it is better to build a model of a *small* type of engine to a large scale. For instance, a 1½-in. scale model of, say, an old Brighton or L.N.W.R. single, or even one of the early G.W.R. broad-gauge engines would give much more satisfaction than, say, an inch-scale model of a Pacific-type engine. The cost, weight and nominal power would be about equal, but the gauge of the 1½ in. engine would be safer and more comfortable for driver and passenger. In addition, the larger gauge would give much less trouble in the matter of steam-raising and maintenance of the locomotive.

Famous historic locomotives of the G.W.R. broad-gauge are worthy of consideration by the model maker. Fig. 9 is an interesting comparison between a 2–4–0 B.G. locomotive designed by Sir Daniel Gooch in 1863 and the present-day "King" class designed by Mr. Charles B. Collett, C.M.E.

TABLE II. WHEEL AND TYRE STANDARDS

(Reference:—Fig. 7.)

Gauge	*BT*	*WT*	*FD*	*FW*
$1\frac{1}{4}$ in.	27·5 mm.	5 mm.	1·5 mm.	1 mm.
$1\frac{3}{4}$ in.	41 mm.	5 mm.	2 mm.	1·25 mm.
2 in.	45·5 mm.	7·5 mm.	2·5 mm.	1·25 mm.
$2\frac{1}{2}$ in.	$2\frac{9}{32}$ in.	$\frac{5}{16}$ in.	$\frac{7}{64}$ in.	$\frac{3}{64}$ in.
$3\frac{1}{4}$ in.	$3\frac{1}{32}$ in.	$\frac{3}{8}$ in.	$\frac{9}{64}$ in.	$\frac{1}{20}$ in.
$3\frac{1}{2}$ in.	$3\frac{9}{32}$ in.	$\frac{9}{32}$ in.	$\frac{9}{64}$ in.	$\frac{1}{20}$ in.
$4\frac{13}{16}$ in.	$4\frac{1}{2}$ in.	$\frac{9}{32}$ in.	$\frac{5}{32}$ in.	$\frac{5}{64}$ in.
5 in.	$4\frac{11}{16}$ in.	$\frac{9}{16}$ in.	$\frac{5}{32}$ in.	$\frac{5}{64}$ in.
$7\frac{1}{4}$ in.	$6\frac{3}{4}$ in.	$\frac{13}{16}$ in.	$\frac{3}{16}$ in.	$\frac{1}{8}$ in.
$9\frac{1}{2}$ in.	9 in.	$1\frac{1}{16}$ in.	$\frac{1}{4}$ in.	$\frac{9}{64}$ in.
$10\frac{1}{4}$ in.	$9\frac{5}{8}$ in.	$1\frac{7}{32}$ in.	$\frac{5}{16}$ in.	$\frac{3}{16}$ in.
15 in.	$13\frac{3}{4}$ in.	$2\frac{1}{8}$ in.	$\frac{3}{4}$ in.	$\frac{7}{16}$ in.

Note: Rails to be laid over-gauge on sharp curves to an amount equal to FW.

For purposes of identification of main-line locomotives built prior to nationalization in 1948, the names or initials of the various railway companies in Great Britain have been retained in this chapter and those following.

Fig. 12.—Model of "Locomotion No. 1" in 7¼-in. gauge on exhibition at Paddington Station, London. Built by B. R. Hunt, Esq., Johannesburg, South Africa, and presented to the directors of G.W.R., 1947.

CHAPTER II

LOCOMOTIVE TYPES

THE model locomotive builder, before he commences the preparation of the working drawings for his proposed engine, should acquaint himself with leading features of the numerous types of locomotives in general use. Even though he has decided on a particular design he should consider carefully the advantages and disadvantages of the chosen design when reproduced to the scale he has adopted for his railway. The various halftones and drawings of actual working models, together with the brief descriptive notes on each class, are intended to assist the reader in this direction.

Fig. 13.—3½-in. gauge 4-4-0 Locomotive. L.S.W.R.

Fig. 14.—Model of a 4-4-0 locomotive. N.E.R.

(Photo: Courtesy of Victor B. Harrison. Esq.)

Fig. 15.—1¾-in. gauge model of the famous G.W.R.
single 4-2-2 "Achilles" during construction.

[13]

Types of Locomotives

Locomotives may be classed generally under two heads:

TENDER ENGINES, which have a separate carriage for fuel and water, and

TANK ENGINES, which are self-contained locomotives with water tank and fuel bunkers all placed on the one frame.

Tender engines are used for long distance passenger or goods trains and tank engines for local passenger, goods and shunting purposes. Large tank engines are also employed for fast passenger-train working in suburban districts.

There are sub-divisions in each class, made according to the work for which they are designed. The illustrated Table III gives particulars of most existing types and the names by which some of the classes are also known, independently of their numerical classification. The centre figures in the notation system indicate the coupled wheels, and those at each end the carrying or bogie wheels. Where no small carrying wheels are present an "0" signifies their absence. The notation presumes that the locomotives have the usual tender unless the suffix "tank" or "T" is employed to denote that they are tank engines.

The 4–4–0 Type

Although at one time the favourite type of locomotive used for express purposes, the 4–4–0 is still generally employed on British Railways. The "Schools" class of the Southern Region is a well known example, with outside cylinders. Usually the cylinders are located between the frames.

The chief objection to the 4–4–0 type is that the length of the firebox is often limited by the distance between the coupled wheels. This objection is not so weighty in the case of small models in which oil or spirit firing is usually adopted as in larger engines where a deep firebox for burning solid fuel is essential.

The smaller model may be provided with a shallow firebox which can be extended backwards and over the trailing axle. However, if a prototype which has a coupled-wheel base of over 9 ft. is modelled no trouble will ensue; more particularly, with outside cylinders the consequent absence of a crank axle

Fig. 16.—Model of the L.N.W.R. locomotive "George V".

enables a slightly longer firebox to be employed. Further, if a high-pitched boiler and moderate-diameter wheels are used an inclined grate will obviate the difficulty.

Outside cylinder engines which drive on to the first pair of coupled wheels are usually arranged (Fig. 13), with the connecting rod inside the coupling rod. This throws the crosshead very close to the tyre of the trailing wheel of the bogie and seriously limits the lateral play required on curves. It is therefore recommended in such cases that in the model the "big end" be connected to the crank pin outside the coupling rod, the centres of the cylinders being extended to suit. This will increase the clearance between the crosshead and the bogie wheel.

(*Courtesy "The Engineer"*)

Fig. 17.—Worsdell's four-coupled express locomotive G.E.R. 1883.

The Four-coupled Six-wheeler (2-4-0 Type)

The four-coupled bogie engine was the outcome of an older and still more English type of locomotive, the 2–4 0 type, as largely used on the old G.E. (Fig. 17) and L.N.W. railways. No advantages can accrue in the matter of flexibility by the copying of this type. However, a fair amount of lateral play may be provided if cylinders with valves on top are employed, and a model locomotive so arranged should be quite as free on a sharp curve as a bogie engine, but would not, perhaps, be quite so steady. In real practice many such engines have leading

Fig. 18.—Mr. J. Ramsbottom's Locomotive "Princess Royal" built at Crewe (L.N.W.R.), 1859. (Drawn by Mrs. E. Howard Steel.)

radial trucks with fairly stiff side controlling springs. Except in locomotives of this type having small driving wheels, a long, deep grate is not practicable.

A firegrate which slopes to the forward end may also be used with advantage in these engines, the back end extending over the trailing axle as already mentioned.

The Six-wheeler-single Type (2-2-2)

The day of the single-wheeled express locomotive is long past. However, in model work very good results can be obtained from such engines, as the weight which may be placed on the driving axle is not limited by considerations of rail strength.

Fig. 18a.—Model 0–4–2 locomotive (1851).

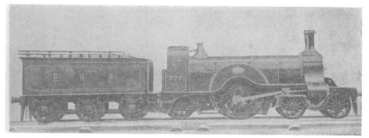

Fig. 19.—Scale model of G.N.R. Stirling single locomotive.

Fig. 20.—A model of the G.W.R. bogie single.

[17]

The engine depicted in Fig. 18 is a model of a six-wheeled single, designed by Mr. J. Ramsbottom for the L.N.W.R. in 1859. Simplicity in construction is perhaps its only feature from a model-maker's point of view. It is a suitable locomotive to model where the builder desires, for reasons of safety and comfort, not only the largest gauge, but, to reduce cost and labour, the smallest possible engine. A 1½ in. or 2 in. scale model, built on the lines of this engine, would be little larger or heavier than a model of a modern 4–6–0 built to a scale of 1 in. to the foot, and would probably prove much less expensive.

In all singles the firebox is more or less unlimited in length and depth. Of course the driving wheels, where they are large in diameter, limit the size of the boiler barrel, but the later rebuilds of the G.C.R. and G.W.R. 7 ft. 8 in. singles, with their high-pitched boilers, show what can be done in the direction of increasing the boiler power of a single.

The 4-2-2 Type

The model of the G.N.R. single (Fig. 19) shows a type of 4–2–2 engine fitted with driving wheels of the largest dimensions ever used in their history, that is to say, 8 ft. 1 in. diameter on tread. The boiler is, of course, limited in all directions except in length of firebox, and in this particular example the trailing wheel of the front bogie has very little lateral play owing to the close proximity of the crosshead and slide bars. In a model the cylinders should be placed a little wider apart than in the proto-type. The lower piston speed of such a large-wheeled engine has to be considered, and if this G.N.R. locomotive is modelled, high-pressure comparatively small-bore cylinders, and efficient superheating are advisable.

The 4-4-2 Type

For fast trains the later developments of locomotive engineering produced the "Atlantic," or 4–4–2, type machines. The "Atlantic" has many of the advantages of the bogie single express engine. The rigidity of the coupled-wheel base is a negligible quantity; the firebox may be lengthened, or, as in the case of the historic G.N.R. No. 251 class, a wide firebox

Fig. 21.—"Atlantic" type model locomotive (4–4–2).

(Wootten type) can be fitted over the trailing carrying wheels. Indeed, the "Atlantic" may be considered as a development of the 4–2–2 type, and the coupled wheels being of moderate diameter, the great drawback of the single wheeler disappears.

The 4–6–0 Type

The 4–6–0 type locomotive is well represented on British Railways. Both the outside and inside cylinder classes are the outcome of a desire for more adhesion and greater heating surface than the 4–4–0 type provides. In the former class the extra coupled wheel is placed between the bogie and the

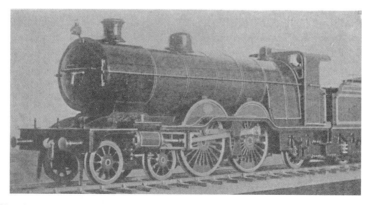

Fig. 22.—Model of the G.N.R. large "Atlantic" type locomotive. The author designed this type of locomotive in 9½-in. gauge (2-in. scale) for Messrs. Bassett-Lowke, Ltd. Northampton.

(Photo: H. Greenly)

Fig. 23.—A Continental "Pacific" locomotive (4-6-2) designed by Roland Martens (Messrs. Krauss & Co.) for the 15-in. gauge "Liliputbahn", Munich in 1924.

driving wheel. In order to reduce the rigid wheel base, the trailing coupling rod may be shortened if small wheels are used. In the inside cylinder class the front end is unchanged. In both classes a shallow grate, at the rear end and sloping forward, is an essential feature; particularly in the case of express engines with large driving wheels.

Numerous models of the 4-6-0 type have been built to the author's designs representing such well known prototypes as the "Royal Scot", "George V", and "Lord Nelson" in gauges ranging from $3\frac{1}{2}$ in. to $10\frac{1}{4}$ in.

Fig. 24.—A model of one of the original American "Atlantics" (4-4-2).

Fig. 25.—No. 1 gauge (1¾-in.) model of the N.Y.C. and H.R.R. "Atlantic" locomotive made by Victor B. Harrison, Esq. from drawings prepared by the author. The model is fired with methylated spirit and fitted with a Smithies' type water-tube boiler.

The 4–6–2 Type

The "Pacific," or 4–6–2 type locomotive, as exemplified by the A10 class (L.N.E.R.) or "Duchess" class (L.M.S.), has some of the characteristics of an "Atlantic" locomotive. The additional pair of coupled wheels are usually placed behind the driving wheels. Under ordinary circumstances the type should only be adopted where the curves of the railway are of

Photo: K. N. Harris, Esq.

Fig. 26.—Chassis for 3½-in. gauge Class 5, 4–6–0 locomotive of the London Midland Region, British Railways. The model is notable for its excellent lubricating system.

[21]

ample radii, and comparatively small driving wheels are an advantage unless the heavier proportions of a modern American engine can be copied. While the increased length of boiler barrel certainly adds to the capacity and length of run, a proportionate degree of added evaporative power must not be expected from the longer tubes.

Goods Locomotives

The 0–6–0 and 0–8–0 type tender goods engines make excellent working models. The relatively small size of the coupled

(Photo: Courtesy of K. N. Harris, Esq. (Kodak Society))

Fig. 27.—A powerful 0–4–2 type passenger-hauling locomotive for a 7¼-in. gauge railway. The engine was built by Mr. A. Rowe, of the Society of Experimental Engineers and Craftsmen.

wheels creates no difficulty at the trailing ends in respect to the firebox. In a six-coupled engine the centre pair of wheels should have thin flanges (or none at all for a model railway with very sharp curves), while the eight-coupled may have flangeless tyres on second pairs of wheels and the trailing wheels arranged with plenty of side play.

The 2–6–0 Type

The "Mogul" type of locomotive is employed on mixed traffic work. The K4 class of the L.N.E.R. is a first-class prototype for a model up to the point where the limitations of the narrow firebox are felt. With outside cylinders a much more

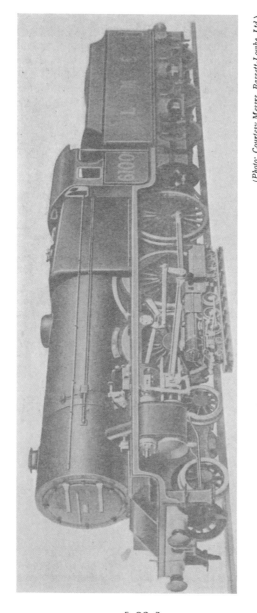

(Photo: *Courtesy Messrs. Bassett-Lowke, Ltd.*)

Fig. 28.—Two models of the famous "Royal Scot", 4–6–0 locomotive of the L.M.S.R. in 7¼-in. and No. 0 gauge.

flexible engine than the standard 0-6-0 can be obtained with very little extra labour.

A modern example of the "Mogul" type of model locomotive is shown in Fig. 45a. The model is built to a scale of $1\frac{1}{2}$ in. to the foot ($\frac{1}{8}$th full size) and is the joint production of Mr. A. C. Schwab, the owner, and Messrs. Greenly Engineering Models, Ltd. The boiler was constructed by Messrs. Goodhand, Gillingham, Kent. The following are leading dimensions and particulars.

Cylinders (two)	2 in. bore by 3 in. stroke.
Total valve travel	0·781 in.
Cut-off in full gear	89 per cent.
Coupled wheels	$8\frac{1}{2}$ in. diameter.
Pony Truck wheels	$4\frac{3}{4}$ in.
Boiler pressure	85 lb./sq. in.
Tubes	18 at $\frac{3}{4}$ in. diameter.
Total Weight (Engine and Tender)	5 cwt.
Tractive Effort at 80 per cent cut off	96 lb.
Estimated total hauling load on level	1 ton 6 cwt.

The 2-6-2 Type

Two classes of this type were used on the L.N.E.R. viz: the V2 (Green Arrow) and V4. The wheel arrangement offers certain advantages in model work, since, with the addition of the trailing axle, a wide firebox of the "Wootten" type can

(*Photo: J. I. Austen-Walton, Esq.*)

Fig. 28a.—5-in. gauge L.M.R. 4-6-0 locomotive "Centaur" made by J. I. Austen-Walton, Esq. ("The Model Engineer" Championship Cup 1947).

Fig. 29.—5-in. gauge G.W.R. "Hall" class locomotive. Built by P. J. E. Spear, Esq., Sutton, Surrey.

be used. The wide firebox is a distinct advantage particularly for models built in the smaller gauges where the size of grate would otherwise be limited to within the frames.

The 2-8-0 Type

The eight-coupled heavy mineral locomotive is being used most extensively on main line railways in Britain. There are the 2800 class of the G.W.R., the 8F class of the L.M.S.R. and the 02 and 04 classes of the L.N.E.R. Mention should also be made of the special freight locomotives evolved by the Ministry of Supply in 1943 for wartime purposes. The addition

Fig. 30.—Canadian 4-6-0 locomotive with an eight-wheeled bogie tender. Built by Messrs. Bassett-Lowke, Ltd. from designs prepared by the author.

[25]

(*Photo: "The Model Engineer"*)

Fig. 31.—5-in. gauge model of a 0-6-0 dock shunting tank locomotive. Built by J. I. Austin-Walton, Esq.

of the extra pair of coupled wheels, as compared with the "Mogul" type, should not present any serious difficulties for modelling purposes. In order to negotiate average curves easily, it is desirable to have flangeless tyres for the second pair of leading coupled wheels.

The 2-8-2 Type

An example of this type is to be found in the L.N.E.R. P2 class ("Lord President") now converted to a Pacific type.

(*Photo: K. N. Harris, Esq.*)

Fig. 32.—Model 2-8-0 British Austerity locomotive "Gillian Diane". Built by G. Jefferies, Esq.

(Photo: K. N. Harris, Esq.)

Fig. 33.—3½-in. gauge four-cylinder L.M.S.R. "Princess Royal" fitted with vacuum brakes. Built by A. Sindens, Esq.

Fig. 34.—Model of a 2–8–2 goods locomotive with outside cylinders and inside valve gear.

Fig. 35.—An experimental small-scale model built by Messrs. Bassett-Lowke, Ltd., to determine the design for a 4–6–4 tank locomotive for the 20-in. Golden Acre Railway, Leeds.

[27]

Fig. 36.—A special 2–10–4 articulated tank locomotive in 2½-in. gauge, originally fitted with a booster. Model constructed by H. P. Jackson, Esq.

The addition of the trailing wheels permits the use of a wide firebox as in the case of the 2–6–2 type. Generally, in selecting an eight coupled type for modelling, the available heating surface of the firebox and tubes must be carefully considered in relation to the comparatively longer boiler barrel applicable to this type.

The 2–10–0 Type

The use of five coupled axles ensured very low loading on the wheels, thus enabling the prototype to be employed on comparatively light tracks. By using a flangeless pair of middle coupled wheels, the engine can be made to negotiate sharper curves. A model worth while modelling in 3½ in. gauge; a 5 in. gauge engine ($\frac{1}{11}$ full size) might be too heavy for convenient handling in the workshop.

Fig. 37.—A 3¾-in. gauge (90 mm.) model of a 4–6–2 locomotive of the Czechoslovakian Railways. The model is fitted with inside admission piston-valve cylinders. Built by A. May, Esq., Prague.

Fig. 38.—Model of a 0–4–4 tank engine.

Tank Locomotives

Tank locomotives are a very general class on railways in this country, and are made in proportions capable of handling long distance suburban trains. The wheels, boiler and cylinder arrangements are often interchangeable with types of tender engines; indeed, many large tank engines are simply tender engines with an extra pair or two pairs of trailing wheels, and the frames arranged to carry side water tanks and a coal bunker.

The advantage of a tank engine in a model is that the whole engine is self contained. No difficulties are met with in regard to the pipes conducting water and fuel to the engine, which in a tender locomotive must be made flexible between

Fig. 39.—Model of a S.E. & C.R. 0–6–4 tank locomotive No. 614.

Fig. 40.—A simple 0–4–0 shunting (Panier) tank locomotive.

Fig. 41.—A G.N.R. 0–4–4 tank locomotive. Built by K. Leech, Esq.

Fig. 42.—7¼-in. gauge American "Hudson" locomotive (4–6–4) designed by the author for the Kenton Miniature Railway.

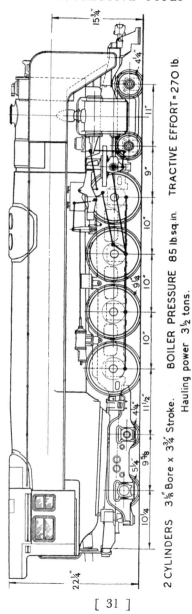

2 CYLINDERS   3⅛″ Bore x 3¾″ Stroke.   BOILER PRESSURE   85 lb. sq. in.   TRACTIVE EFFORT=270 lb.

Hauling power 3½ tons.

Fig. 43.—Design for a 7¼-in. gauge model of the 4–8–4 locomotive (Niagara type) N.Y.C.R. The design of the model, prepared by E. A. Steel, Esq., is similar to the Greenly "Mountain" type built to the same scale in 1936.

engine and tender. The use of a closed cab, however, introduces some drawbacks in firing a solid fuel model. A removable cab roof or back plate is usually found to be the best solution to this difficulty.

One interesting and useful type of tank or tender engine is the front coupled engine. It can be recommended as a large-scale garden-railway model where first cost and time in construction are to be saved. Such a model tank engine in $7\frac{1}{4}$ in. or $9\frac{1}{2}$ in. gauge is only a few feet long, and can be driven with ease from a following truck. A large garden is sufficient to

(Photo: V. B. Harrison, Esq.)

Fig. 44.—Model 2-6-4 G.W.R. type tank locomotive, No. 1 gauge (spirit fired).

accommodate a continuous railway. A development of this front-coupled type of tank locomotive, viz, the 0-4-4 engine, is to be found in the M7 class of the Southern Region. It has the advantage over the smaller front-coupled engine in that the bunker is larger, and should therefore be adopted in preference for smaller gauges. The 2-4-2 type engine is quite as good as the 0-4-4, but suffers in the matter of limitations of firebox equally with the 4-4-0 tender engine. The same applies to the 4-4-2 model. However, in tank engines the driving wheels are usually of reduced diameter, and the firebox can therefore be extended backwards over the trailing coupled axle.

The characteristics of the 0-6-2 and 0-8-2 tank engines are those of the six-coupled and eight-coupled tender goods engines. The bunker room on such engines is usually ample.

Although it is not a known prototype on British Railways, a 4-4-2 type tank engine with outside cylinders driving on

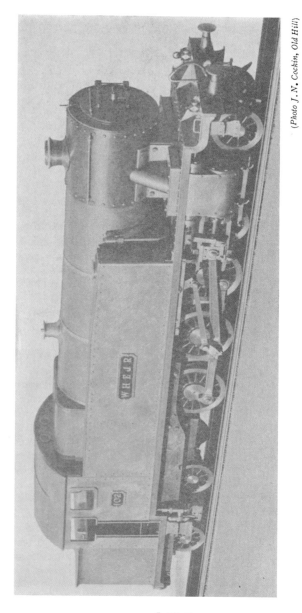

(*Photo J. N. Cockin, Old Hill*)

Fig. 45.—5-in. gauge free-lance "Halton" tank locomotive built by J. H. Westwood, Esq., Old Hill, Staffs. (Special features of the design are the outside frames at the rear to permit the fitting of a Wide Firebox and Walschaerts' Valve Gear.)

[33]

to the trailing coupled wheel would make a good engine for a road with sharp curves.

The 2–6–4 or 4–6–4 type outside-cylinder engine is perhaps the best type of passenger or mixed-traffic tank engine that a model-maker could design where solid fuel is to be used. The firebox can be made of almost any width or length, and the flexibility of the wheel base is remarkable. In fact, side controlling springs are necessary in the trailing bogie to ensure stability on the straight track. Otherwise the engine might tend to travel crab fashion. Alternatively by employing a leading bogie, a 4–6–4, or "Baltic" tank engine, could be substituted.

Articulated Locomotives

There are several types of articulated locomotives worthy of consideration in miniature where greater power, coupled with flexibility of wheelbase is specially required. The boiler usually spans between two sets of frames, coupled wheels and engine units. A feature of the "Mallet" system of articulation is the proximity of the cylinders to the boiler; which is especially

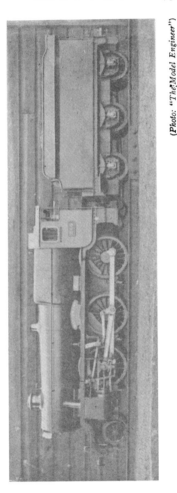

Fig. 45a.—Mr. A. C. Schwab's G.W. type 2–6–0 locomotive for the 7¼-in. gauge Saltwood Miniature Railway, Hythe, Kent.

(Photo: "The Model Engineer")

desirable in a working model. This type is usually designed as a compound—the front pair of cylinders for low pressure and the rear pair of cylinders for high pressure work.

TABLE III

CLASSIFICATION OF LOCOMOTIVES

	0—4—0	Shunting Tank Engines
	0—4—2	Tank Engine
	0—4—4	Surban Tank.
	2—2—2	Six-wheeled Single.
	4—2—2	Bogie Single.
	2—4—0	Old Express Locomotive.
	4—4—0	Four-coupled Bogie.
	4—6—0	Six-coupled Bogie.
	4—6—2	"Pacific" Type.
	4—4—2	"Atlantic" Type.
	0—6—0	Six-Coupled Goods or Tank.
	0—8—0	British Eight-coupled Goods.
	2—6—0	"Mogul" Goods.
	2—8—0	"Consolidation" Goods or Tank.
	2—10—0	"Decapod" Goods.
	2—8—2	Goods or Tank.
	0—6—2	Usually Goods Tank.
	2—6—4	Usually Tank Engines.
	4—8—2	Heavy Goods.

4—8—2 + 2—8—4 }
2—6—0 + 0—6—2 } Beyer-Garratt

2—6—2   Mixed Traffic or Tank.

0—10—0   British Banking Engine.

4—8—4   "Niagara" Type.

4—8—8—4   U.S. Articulated.

2—8—4   South African Railways.

The "Garret" type locomotive can best be described as a boiler and cab on a girder frame bridging a leading water tender unit and a trailing unit for both fuel and water. A set of high pressure cylinders and coupled wheels are provided for each unit.

A third type of articulated locomotive is the "Modified Fairlie" with its boiler carried between two complete engine units.

The author has evolved an articulated tank engine (Fig. 36) which has only one motor "bogie". The point of articulation is directly under the smokebox.

[35]

Fig. 46.—No. 1 gauge articulated Reichsbahn tank locomotive designed for burning solid fuel. The model was built by V. B. Harrison, Esq., to the author's design.

A notable fact in connection with the articulated class of locomotive generally is its usefulness in full-size practice on the narrower gauge railways where axle loadings are restricted but a maximum hauling power is a necessity.

Free-Lance Designs

The choice of prototype for the model engineer to reproduce in miniature as a working scale model is almost limitless. The model need not be an exact replica of any particular well-known type but can be an entirely free and independent design to suit the designer. It should not, of course, be too fanciful and impracticable, but should be able to stand alongside its more orthodox confrères without appearing odd or clumsy.

Special attention should be given to free-lance designs employed in the larger gauges for passenger-hauling in pleasure parks and estates.

An example of free-lance design having certain well-known characteristics of the G.W.R. is shown in Fig. 45. The locomotive was designed by the author in 1930 and this particular model has been been built by Mr. J. H. Westwood, Old Hill, Staffs. The principal dimensions are given below:

Cylinders: (Piston-valves) ..	$1\frac{1}{2}$-in. bore by $2\frac{1}{4}$-in. stroke.
Coupled wheels	5-in. diam.
Bogie Wheels	$3\frac{1}{2}$-in. diam.
Boiler Pressure	85 lb./sq. in.
Tractive Effort	75 lb.
Weight	3 cwt.

Modern Developments

In view of the research and developments taking place in the locomotive world to-day, further scope and interest is given the model engineer to reproduce in miniature the new engines that are being introduced on main-line railways. One well-known British class of locomotive deserves attention, viz.: the "West Country" class of the Southern Region. There are features of the design which could be incorporated in a $\frac{3}{4}$ in. or 1 in. scale model to some advantage, otherwise details such as the valve gear may have to be simplified to suit a working model.

Experiments might also be carried out on a small model of Mr. O. V. Bulleid's "Leader" class of the same Region. But this is one which should be tackled only by a model engineer with the experience of a number of orthodox designs behind him—particularly if the locomotive is to be built in any gauge larger than $3\frac{1}{2}$ in.

Finally this chapter would not be complete without some mention of the steam turbine locomotive. An example of this type is the L.M.S.R. 4–6–2 "Pacific" engine with its geared drive to the leading coupled wheels.[1] The turbine unit is fitted below the smokebox and develops 2,000 h.p. Turbine design is, however, a wholly separate subject of study, as distinct from the design of reciprocating engines described in the following pages. In model work 1 in. scale is about the smallest size to be recommended for a locomotive of this type if serious experimental work is to be undertaken in this direction. A design for a small unit is given in Chapter V, page 71.

With the introduction of standard types of locomotives by British Railways, further interest has been stimulated among model engineers to build the new 4–6–2, 4–6–0 and 2–6–0 tender locomotives, and a 2–6–4 tank engine of modern design. All these engines are well suited for building in any of the standard model gauges. The remarks concerning the various types of engines discussed earlier in this chapter are equally applicable to those of modern design.

[1] Formerly L.M.S.R. locomotive No. 6202, converted to four-cylinder locomotive and named "Princess Anne".

[37]

CHAPTER III

THE PRINCIPLES OF MODEL LOCOMOTIVE DESIGN

It is presumed that the reader is acquainted with the action of the piston in the cylinder of the locomotive and with the mechanism employed to transmit the work done to the wheels of the engine. From this point, study should be made of the various means of reversing, and an understanding of the functions of the slide valve obtained, but before proceeding to such detail it is necessary to know something of the principles involved in estimating the power of a locomotive.

Draw-bar Effort

A locomotive is required not only to move itself, but to propel a train; only the power which is delivered to the train is useful. While the horse-power of a locomotive is sometimes calculated, particulars of its "draw-bar pull" is much more useful knowledge.

For a goods engine travelling at low speeds a high initial draw-bar effort is required. In an express engine it is desirable that this pull on the train should be maintained at the highest speeds. For this reason larger driving wheels are adopted for express engines. In goods engines the draw-bar pull is increased at the expense of speed, by using small-diameter coupled wheels in conjunction with cylinders of the same dimensions as those of a passenger-train engine of equal power.

There is a limit to the number of revolutions that a wheel and its attendant machinery will attain, and the economical speed of a goods engine is therefore low. If accelerated beyond that speed the whole of the power developed will be absorbed in moving the mechanism of the engine and in rolling resistance.

Engines with small driving wheels are, as a general rule, more successful models than those with large wheels. For a given speed the revolutions per minute of the driving wheels is higher and condensation losses, particularly for the small scale model, are thereby reduced.

[38]

Rolling Resistance of Model Trains

The rolling resistance of a model train varies with the size, and while the diameter of the driving wheel does not affect the question of draw-bar pull so much in a model as in the full-size prototype, the principle remains true.

To enable the reader to estimate the load a model will haul it may be said that 1 lb. draw-bar pull will be sufficient to start a 25 lb. train, in small sizes, and in larger engines the ratio varies from 1 in 30 to 1 in 35.

The following summary gives the resistances that have to be overcome before a locomotive can be said to be doing useful work.

ENGINE AND TENDER

Frictional:

Piston Rings	Valve motion pin joints
Gland packings	Axle bearings
Slides	Pumps, etc.
Valves	Wheel flanges against rails
Connecting rod Bearings	Journals
Coupling rod Bearings	Rolling friction

In addition other factors of resistance have to be taken into account, viz: acceleration, rotational inertia, gradients, curves and wind resistance. The student of engineering is recommended

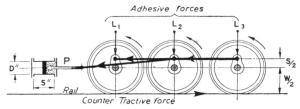

Fig. 47.—Forces applied to produce tractive effort.
    (1) Force P on piston transmitted to coupled wheels.
    (2) Adhesive loads on axles L1, L2 and L3.
    (3) Frictional contact between wheels and Rails.
    (4) Ratio of wheel diameter and piston stroke =S/W.

to study the specialized textbooks of locomotive engineering for more detailed accounts of the subject.

The formula universally employed for estimating the tractive effort of a "two-cylinder simple" locomotive is—

$$\text{Tractive force in lb.} = \frac{D^2 \times S \times P}{W}$$

Where

D is the cylinder bore in inches
W is the driving-wheel diameter in inches
S is the length of stroke in inches
P is the boiler pressure in lb. per square inch.

It is also usual to reckon on the basis of only 70% or 80% of the boiler pressure. In small model work 60% may be adopted.

For four-cylinder compound engines the formula is altered by substituting for the factor D^2:

$$\text{the value } 2\,H^2 - \frac{H^4}{L^2}$$

Where H is the high-pressure cylinder diameter
L ,, low- ,, ,, ,,
(Two-cylinder compounds would be half this value.)

For four "simple" cylinders the tractive effort will be twice as much as the first formula above states.

By the use of the above formula not only can the values of various dimensions of cylinders and driving wheels be compared, but the proper ratio of tractive force and weight on the coupled wheels may be determined. In real locomotive practice the maximum tractive effort is generally arranged to bear a proportion of 1 in 4 or 4½ of the weight available for adhesion, that is, the total weight on all coupled wheels. In small work the author has found that slipping will not occur on a dry rail if the tractive force does not exceed ⅓ of the adhesive weight, and as a guide to the probable weights reference should be made to the locomotive weights given in Table I. From these weights the loads on coupled axles can be proportioned in the same ratio as in real practice.

The adhesive weight of tank engines depends upon the quantity of water in the side tanks. Therefore, a larger factor

of adhesion should be allowed than in the case of tender locomotives to provide for low-water conditions.

The Size of the Cylinders

The size of the cylinders of a model locomotive should not
be finally fixed without due consideration of other points, otherwise the cylinders may prove to be so small that a very high

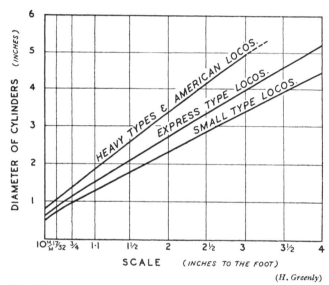

(*H. Greenly*)

**Fig. 48.—Diagram showing nominal cylinder proportions
for various gauges. (Two Cylinders).**

steam pressure is required to do the necessary duty, or so large as
to drain the boiler unduly of steam. An excessively high steam-
pressure is wasteful in the following respects:
- (a) There will be increased leakage past piston and valve-
    spindle glands, etc.
- (b) The temperature of the steam becomes excessive, par-
    ticularly if it is superheated, and as a result lubrication
    may prove difficult.
- (c) A stronger and heavier boiler is required. This condition
    will be found to reduce efficiency.

Of course, high pressure is a lesser evil than a very low one, because—

(d) A low pressure involves a large volume and violent ebullition. Consequently priming (which produces a still further disturbance in the boiler) may occur if the cylinders are of too large capacity.

(e) A given volume of steam at low pressure contains less heat than the same volume at a higher pressure.

Cylinder condensation, which has a cumulative effect, may therefore be induced by the use of too low a pressure. Furthermore, it must be borne in mind that the temperature of the steam varies with the pressure, and a low pressure means that the steam is nearer the liquefaction point per unit volume.

To enable the reader to determine the size of the cylinder for any given gauge, the curves shown in diagram Fig. 48 may be used. The three values for (1) large-model built to American loading gauge, (2) modern express engine, (3) small shunting engine or historic model with small boiler, are represented by the different curves. The cylinder capacity may, of course, be

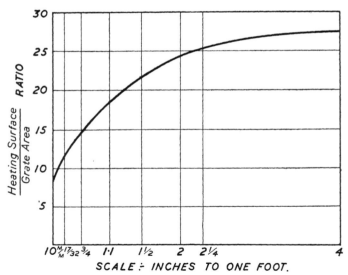

Fig. 49.—Heating surface/grate area ratios for various gauges.

always added to in proportion to any increase of heating surface over the normal, always provided that such addition to heating surface is attended by a proportionate increase in grate area. In fact, the whole success of a model locomotive, assuming an equal quality of workmanship, choice of suitable material, and soundness in design and construction of the boiler, depends on the ratio of grate area, heating surface and cylinder capacity.

In order to obviate the use of formulæ a few values are given in Table IV for boiler proportions. The diagram (Fig. 49) shows the trend of heating surface grate area ratios for various scales.

TABLE IV

WATER-TUBE BOILER PROPORTIONS

Gauge of Locomotive inches	*Inside Boiler inches*	*Outer Shell inches*	*Heating Surface sq. in.*	*Water Tubes*	
				No.	*Diam. in.*
$1\frac{3}{4}$	$1\frac{3}{4}$	$2\frac{3}{8}$	50	3	$\frac{1}{4}$
$1\frac{3}{4}$	$1\frac{7}{8}$	$2\frac{1}{2}$	60	4	$\frac{1}{4}$
$2\frac{1}{2}$	2	3	70	4	$\frac{1}{4}$
$2\frac{1}{2}$	$2\frac{1}{4}$	$3\frac{1}{4}$	80	5	$\frac{1}{4}$
$3\frac{1}{2}$	$2\frac{7}{8}$	4	90	5	$\frac{1}{4}$
$3\frac{1}{2}$	3	$4\frac{1}{4}$	110	7	$\frac{1}{4}$

Working Pressures: 40 lb. to 60 lb. sq. in.

Wet and Dry Steam Compared

One other point which is very important to the success of the model locomotive involves a practice which the writer has constantly advocated. In a model steam engine the highest degree of superheat the material of the cylinder will allow should be employed. In small engines fitted with brass or gunmetal cylinders this degreee of super-heat is not particularly high, and may not be more than necessary to maintain dry steam. Wet steam is very conducive to cylinder condensation.

The writer has found that attempts to take advantage of the expansive force of steam are not usually attended with any overall economy in very small models, therefore calculations of probable steam consumption based on an early cut-off are not attained in practice, and should not be considered.

TABLE V

LOCO-TYPE BOILER PROPORTIONS

Gauge in.	Type	Diam. in.	Heating Surface sq. in.	Grate Area sq. in.	H.S. / G.A.	Pressure p.s.i.	Remarks
1¾	Wide Firebox	2½	65	7	9·3	40	"Continental Tank"
2½	Wide Firebox	3	165	11	15	60	
3½	Pacific	4¼	450	24	18·75	75	
3½	Wide Firebox	4¼	300	22	13·65	70	
5	4-6-0	6	550	27	20·4	80	
5	Wide Firebox	6	1,040	58	18	85	
7¼	4-6-0	9	1,200	62	19·5	90	"Royal Scot"
7¼	American	11	3,210	147	21·8	100	"Hudson" Type
7¼	Pacific	9	3,000	100	30	95	
10¼	4-6-0	13	3,675	122	30	110	"Royal Scot"
15	4-6-2	22⅝	17,850	677	26·4	175	R.H. and D. Rlwy.

The theoretical mean effective pressure (m.e.p.) is based on the formula

$$P = \frac{p_1}{r} (1 + \log_e r) - P_b$$

where P = mean effective pressure, lb. per sq. in. abs.
p_1 = initial pressure, lb. per sq. in. abs.
p_b = back pressure, lb. per sq. in. abs.
r = ratio of expansion.

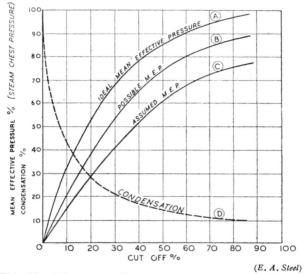

(E. A. Steel)

Fig. 50.—The mean effective pressure in a cylinder for various cut-offs.

The curve "A", Fig. 50 indicates the "ideal" m.e.p. for various cut-offs. But condensation losses and pressure drop must be taken into consideration so that the curve of m.e.p.s. is lowered to "B" even under the best conditions. For very small models the curve "C" is more applicable and shows the falling off of effective pressure on the piston head at the lower cut-offs. The curve "D" indicates also the rapid rise of condensation as cut-off is reduced.

Compounding also shows little or no economy in steam or fuel. Steam engineers are well aware of the great increase in cylinder condensation which follows attempts to expand steam

[45]

in a single cylinder. The model engine is an extremely wasteful steam user, and this is in a large measure due to the following circumstances:

The surface of a solid body does not vary in a direct ratio to its capacity. The cooling surfaces of a model cylinder are therefore much greater in proportion to its capacity than that obtaining in a full-size engine. To emphasize this fact, and to show one cause of the excessive cylinder condensation present in a model, the diagram (Fig. 51) has been prepared.

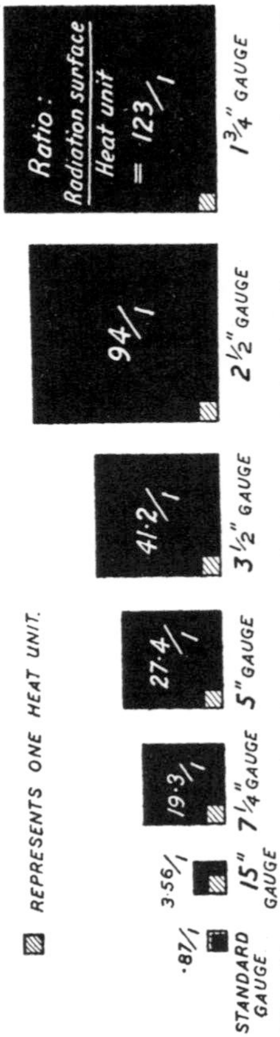

For a full size locomotive, sufficient heat is available for doing useful work and to cover losses due to radiation, viz: 1,960 B.Th.U's in an area of 1,700 square inches. (Ratio 0·87/1). For model engines the proportions are entirely different. Thus, for a No. 1 gauge cylinder the ratio is of the order of 123/1 and for a 7¼ in. gauge cylinder it is 19·3/1.

The diagrams are proportioned to a given amount of cooling surface and show the relatively small amount of heat that is available for doing useful work.

Cylinder Condensation

Cylinder condensation in a greater or lesser degree being inevitable, the question resolves itself into one of palliatives. A reduction in heat losses may be obtained by—

(1) Increasing the pressure. Success will accompany this up to a certain point. In any case, scale pressures must be exceeded. In a ½-in. scale model $\frac{1}{24}$ of the

Fig. 51.—Diagram showing why cylinder condensation is excessive in small models compared with a full-size prototype. It will be noted that for a one gauge model the minute quantity of heat available per stroke can be easily lost to the comparatively large radiation surface. The losses are lessened as the scale of the model is increased.

real locomotive pressure (i.e. $\frac{1}{24}$ of 240 lb. = 10 lb. per sq. in.) would be of no practical use.

(2) Superheating or drying the steam. Superheating is a term given to the heating of steam to a temperature above the normal at which steam at any given pressure is generated.

(3) Lagging all parts containing steam with non-conducting material, such as felt or flannel, or asbestos.

(4) Increasing the piston speed. This can be done by using a smaller driving wheel and employing cylinders with a long stroke.

Steam Pressures

Reverting to the subject of steam pressures in small models, the boilers are often unlagged and a very high pressure is not likely to prove so economical as a moderate one owing to the greater difference between the temperature of the boiler and that of the atmosphere. All boilers, therefore, should be lagged —whether they have to work indoors or outside in all weathers.

Only on large engines, i.e. $1\frac{1}{2}$ in. scale and upwards, can any saving in steam be effected by linking up. But economy is only obtained where linking up is combined with efficient steam drying or superheating. When steam is expanded lique-faction occurs—more heavily where only saturated steam is used—and if a large cylinder with the valve cutting off at a point too early in the stroke is used, cylinder condensation will assume a high proportion and all the expected economy will disappear, if the engine is not rendered a failure.

In such cases where an existing engine with large cylinders has to be made to work successfully, the ill-effects of cylinder condensation may be mitigated by superheating and wire-drawing the steam by using a very small port in the regulator. This will also tend to superheat the steam and prevent priming which latter always attends excessive cylinder condensation.

Compounding

Compounding will not increase efficiency very much, if at all. A compound system should only be used on large models, and where the use of four cylinders is desired.

The two-cylinder system of compounding would appear to

offer a good chance of success, but it is quite out of date. Next to this the Smith three-cylinder system (one high pressure and two low pressure cylinders) is suitable for model locomotive work, but requires three sets of valve motion. The steam pressure of a model compound locomotive should not be less than 70 to 80 lb. per square inch. The cut-off should, in full gear, be as near to 85% of the stroke as possible. Re-superheating may be adopted for the middle stage (i.e. receiver stage). The ratio of the cylinder capacity should not exceed 1 to $2\frac{1}{4}$. Unless very high pressures are available an early cut-off in the high-pressure cylinder will be fatal to success.

The Point of Cut-off

In all two-cylinder simple locomotives it is essential that the point of cut-off shall not be less than 80% of the stroke in full gear to ensure starting. An earlier cut-off is obtained by linking up the reversing gear. The effect of linking up is to make the engine run with less "knock," and large model engines are always linked up when once under way. Any economy obtained by this means of expanding the steam is quite as high in a model as that which would result from an efficient compound system.

CHAPTER IV

BOILER DESIGN

ALTHOUGH great liberties may be taken with regard to the proportions of a model locomotive boiler, the same care as that exercised in real practice must be taken in providing means to ensure the maximum evaporation of the water, viz., in smokebox arrangements, grate area, furnace capacity, tube area, steam tightness and in the completeness of the combustion of the fuel. All these features and functions are more important where the orthodox type of generator, known as the "loco-type boiler," is adopted. Again, the dimensions of the boiler of a railway engine are bounded by certain limits of height, length and width, and the designer of the model will be handicapped in the same way as locomotive engineers of this country are at the present time. The adoption of the American loading gauge would, of course, help the model-maker. The same advantage is present when a model is based on the overall dimensions of one of the Colonial narrow-gauge systems.

In designing a model locomotive, it may be said that all types have merits and demerits in strict accordance with the manner in which the wheel, frame and cylinder arrangements affect the boiler, more particularly with reference to the proportions of firebox and the methods of firing.

The Simple Boiler

With regard to the simple "pot" boilers fitted to toy steam locomotives and to small engines in No. 0 gauge, it may be said that their success is entirely due to the use of a well-ventilated and relatively large flame of a spirit burner and boiler shells constructed of thin material. The last is a very important item. The overall efficiency of these boilers is low, but with cylinders made with extreme care and delicacy such engines are made to work very successfully. Any attempt to copy such models in a rough, amateurish manner with heavy tubes and castings is doomed to failure. There is a middle course, by

E   [49]

using a thin copper silver-soldered boiler with one or more water tubes, which will be considered later. It must, however, be noted that the above type of model, although it may have the exhaust conducted up the chimney, does not require or avail itself of that essential function of a real locomotive, namely, the inductive action of the exhaust steam on the fire. The flame of the "outside-fired engine" either burns in open air or the draught is a natural one.

The Diameter of the Boiler

Returning to the "scale model," the first problem that arises is in the diameter of the boiler. The diagram (Fig. 52)

Fig. 52.—Diagram showing restrictions due to loading and rail gauges. A. Boiler between large coupled wheels. B. Modern boiler set above coupled wheels but limited to within maximum loading gauge. C. Boiler with wide firebox astride a pony truck (as in the case of a modern "Pacific" type).

shows the three main conditions arising from restrictions in rail gauge. The early single-wheel express engine had (due to its large wheel diameter and low-pitched boiler) a barrel limited by the distance between the tyres, as at A. The sketch B shows the normal conditions now obtaining in coupled express loco-motives. The diameter of the boiler barrel is bounded by the top of the driving wheel flanges and therefore, with a given gauge, by the height of its centre line and the diameter of the driving wheels. In the case of a goods engine the wheels do not affect the boiler barrel, but in the matter of firebox width greater freedom is obtained. With reference to the sketch C, where the firebox is entirely clear of coupled wheels, the same arrangement may be adopted. The carrying wheels would be of small diameter, special designs of main frames being used under the firebox.

The ideal requirements of a model boiler are as follows:

(1) It should provide for a good circulation of the water.

(2) Proper ventilation of the fire to ensure complete combustion.

(3) The largest possible range of water levels and a sufficient capacity for a good reserve of steam.

(4) Furnace or firebox should be ample, the definition of the word "ample" depending on the type of boiler and fuel used, also the size of the model.

(5) Efficient smokebox arrangements, with due regard to the fuel employed.

(6) The plates and thickness of tubes should not be heavier than necessary. Unless this recommendation is observed it is impossible to steam a locotype boiler efficiently (or its equivalent with a methylated spirit lamp). This fault, in conjunction with a neglect of the induced draught of the exhaust, was the cause of all the early failures.

(7) Reduction in the number of joints, and, in the case of copper loco-type boilers especially, good fitting.

(8) Equal strength in all parts, with a factor of safety varying from 6 to 10.

Types of Boilers

Model locomotive boilers may be divided into four types:

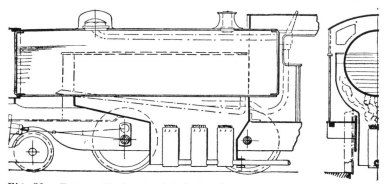

Fig. 53.—Externally fired spirit boiler for a tank locomotive. Steam is collected in the dome and controlled by a simple plug-cock type regulator in the cab. Some degree of superheat is provided by passing the steam pipe over the burners and thence to cylinders.

[51]

(a) the plain cylindrical pot-boiler, (b) the water-tube boiler which was invented by Mr. F. Smithies in 1900 and with the early development of which the writer had much to do, (c) the loco-type boiler, and (d) the flash steam generator.

Outside-fired Boilers

With regard to the first type, supplementing the remarks already made as to the necessity for extreme lightness, it is essential that such boilers should be heated over their whole length, and that the barrel should be pitched as high as possible above the level of the rails, otherwise there will not be sufficient height for the flame of the lamp. The vaporizing lamp (this

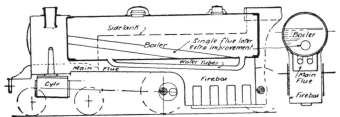

Fig. 54.—A simple type of water-tube boiler with enclosed spirit "firebox". A flue tube is fitted from firebox to front boiler plate. Additional water tubes are also provided in the bottom of the boiler barrel.

lamp does not work well under a fierce induced draught, therefore difficulties may occur if it is applied to internally fired engines) is perhaps the best of all spirit burners for this purpose. This question of height is the one difficulty in making scale working models in No. 0 (1¼ in.) gauge. Free-lance types of locomotives are therefore usually chosen in this gauge.

Fig. 53 shows the arrangement for a plain cylindrical boiler. A tank engine with long side tanks is adopted, and the latter are used to conceal the flame of the lamp, which, of course, burns under natural draught. One or two water tubes may be added, but to allow these to be used all joints should be silver soldered.

Water-tube Boilers

An arrangement of a water-tube boiler with a single flue tube is shown in Fig. 54. It consists of a plain cylindrical boiler, one

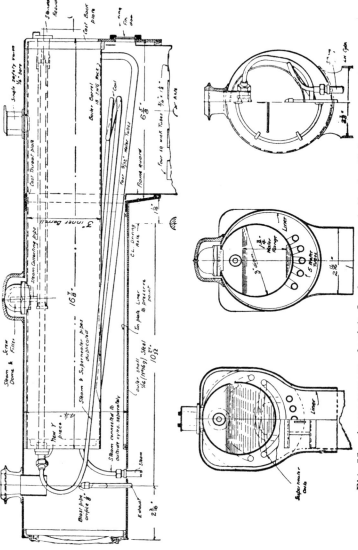

Fig. 55.—Arrangement of spirit-fired water-tube boiler for 3¼-in. gauge models.

or more water tubes with an enclosed furnace and a rectangular flue fitted to the underside. A plain spirit lamp is used, and the whole is fitted to a $3\frac{1}{4}$-in. gauge engine. Induced draught is employed. The scheme is of no great value for locomotives under $2\frac{1}{2}$ in. gauge owing to restriction in flame height, unless abnormal proportions for the locomotive are adopted.

A characteristic of the water-tube boiler is the simplicity of the boiler proper and its encasement in a shell having the usual external features of the loco-type generator. Another point of intrinsic value is that the whole of the boiler is encased in the heated gases, the loss of heat by radiation through the outer casing not affecting the steaming of the boiler in any way.

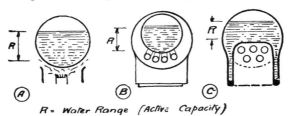

R = Water Range (Active Capacity)

Fig. 56.—Diagram showing the range of permissible evaporation for simple, water-tube and internally-fired boilers respectively.

Of course, the use of water tubes ensures excellent end-to-end circulation. A drawback to this type of generator is the burning of the paint or enamel which occurs where boiler casings are not lined with a separate shell, especially near the firebox. To get over troubles in this connection a *thick* inner casing of sheet iron, covered with a thin brass lagging is used, the space between, where the two casings touch, being packed with asbestos to reduce conduction. Where a metal lining is impossible a heavy-gauge material for the outside casing can be used It can be protected at the firebox end with a lining of asbestos. It is essential to success in all cases to provide the lightest inner boiler shell and tubes consistent with strength factors, that can be worked.

Fig. 55 shows various sections of a water-tube type loco-motive boiler for all gauges from "0" to $3\frac{1}{4}$ in.

The diagram, Fig. 56 shows the relative water capacities of three types of boilers, and remembering its extreme simplicity

[54]

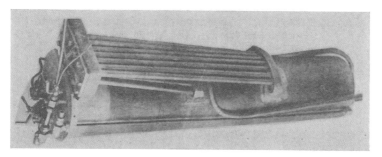

Fig. 57.—Early type of model water-tube boiler fitted with water tubes and downcomer in the firebox.

and rapid steaming, the water-tube boiler has a wide water range. In small scales the plain outside firebox cannot be made as large as otherwise desirable because of the height above wick level required for the flame. Fig. 57 shows another type of water-tube boiler built to the author's design with straight tubes fitted with downcomer and upcomers.

The following are conditions which tend towards success in a model locomotive water-tube boiler:

(1) Narrow firebox of the greatest length rather than width. This is especially important where a spirit wick lamp is used. The barrel should not be too long. A good proportion is one where the firebox length is not less than that of the barrel.

(2) Proportions of inner and outer barrel should in no case exceed 3 to 4 (measuring inside the outer barrel), while a ratio of from 2 to 3 or 5 to 7 gives the best results. Always increase the diameter of the outer casing in preference to the inner one.

(3) The boiler should not be crowded with water-tubes. A well ventilated flame should be obtained when, during the period of steam raising, on opening the smokebox door the boiler is found to be working under natural draught. This more or less applies to spirit-burning engines of $2\frac{1}{2}$ in. gauge, and smaller, where auxiliary methods of inducing a draught are considered troublesome. Small gauge locomotives

[55]

work well with from two to five $\frac{1}{4}$-in. or $\frac{3}{16}$-in. water tubes, which should be of thin gauge material. The use of a cast downcomer is not essential, and a cast back-plate is a matter of convenience for screwing in fittings rather than an aid to efficiency.

Caution.—Readers are advised that the fumes emitted with the exhaust of a spirit-fired engine are poisonous. Discomfort, as well as expense, therefore, is present where this fuel is used

Fig. 57a.—Locomotive-type boiler for $7\frac{1}{4}$-in. gauge "Pacific".

indoors in such a way that it is not completely burnt, whereas there is little or no danger with a charcoal fire.

Loco-type Boilers

The locomotive-type fire-tube boiler has almost superseded the water-tube boiler in all gauges with the possible exception of No. 1 gauge. Solid fuel is very manageable, and with a well-made and proportioned boiler, efficient cylinders and proper blast arrangements, success is assured.

A successful loco-type boiler may be obtained by—

(1) A large grate area.

(2) A large boiler diameter to provide sufficient tube heating surface and ample range of water. The diameter should, if possible, be above normal. In smaller models length is not a drawback where solid fuel is used, as it helps the water range of the boiler.

(3) With a coal fire a deep grate at the tube-plate end is desirable. Where charcoal is used the fuel may be heaped, and therefore the total capacity of the furnace

is important. With coal the capacity below the level of the tubes or "brick arch" line should be considered.

(4) The inner firebox plates and the tubes should be of the thinnest material consistent with strength, handling in construction and resistance to corrosion. All flat surfaces must be stayed, and except in the smallest sizes little or no allowance should be made for the natural stiffness of the plates in calculating the amount of support given by the stays.

(5) Tubes should be neatly spaced, the following being suitable sizes (Table VI).

TABLE VI

DIMENSIONS OF BOILER TUBES

Gauge in.	Diameter in.	Thickness in.	Material
$1\frac{3}{4}$	$\frac{5}{16} - \frac{3}{8}$	20 s.w.g.	Copper
$2\frac{1}{2}$	$\frac{3}{8} - \frac{7}{16}$	20 s.w.g.	Copper
$3\frac{1}{2}$	$\frac{3}{8} - \frac{9}{16}$	18 s.w.g.	Copper
5	$\frac{7}{16} - \frac{5}{8}$	18 or 16 s.w.g.	Copper
$7\frac{1}{4}$	$\frac{5}{8} - \frac{3}{4}$	16 s.w.g.	Copper
$9\frac{1}{2}$	$\frac{3}{4} - \frac{7}{8}$	15 s.w.g.	Steel
$10\frac{1}{4}$	$\frac{7}{8}$	15 s.w.g.	Steel
15	$1\frac{1}{8} - 1\frac{3}{8}$	11 s.w.g.	Steel

(6) Where long tubes are necessary, employ the larger diameter stated. Water tubes in the firebox are only desirable where oil burners (or spirit) are employed for firing.

(7) The heating surface should not be obtained at the expense of the water and steam spaces at the sides of the firebox and above the crown. In small boilers the level of the crown should be below the centre line of the boiler, and only in the larger models above this level (see Fig. 58).

(8) In small engines the adoption of a higher pressure than that really required by the cylinders is an advantage provided means such as the use of a small regulator

orifice are provided to keep the pressure back in the boiler. This "wire-drawing" of the steam tends to superheat the supply and also prevents violent ebullition in the boiler which either attends or creates priming and excessive cylinder condensation. An unsuccessful over-cylindered engine may often be made workable in this way, possibly with the addition of a good superheater and a sharp blast.

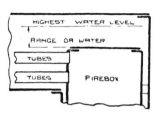 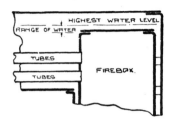

Fig. 58.—Diagram showing (a) the correct height of a firebox crown; and (b) a crown rising too high into the boiler thus limiting the range of water level.

(9) Efficient smokebox arrangements are indispensable to complete combustion of solid fuel. The smokebox must be quite airtight in order that a partial vacuum is created by the blast.

Blast Pipes

The critical point of steam generation in a model locomotive is the size of orifice in the blast pipe. It will be found that a slight modification in the diameter of the orifice will make a difference to the steaming capacity of the engine. The ratio of the cross-sectional area of the nozzle to the cross-sectional area of the cylinder varies according to the size of the model. In full-size practice the ratio is approximately 1 to 15. For very small models a ratio of 1 to 30 can be adopted and for larger engines 1 to 20 or 25. The sizes of orifices for various sizes of cylinders, based on the above ratios, are given in Table XIII.

The position of the blast pipe orifice must be located in its correct position below the centre-line of the chimney. The blast will not function efficiently if placed in the exact scale position of its prototype. It should be placed at a point below

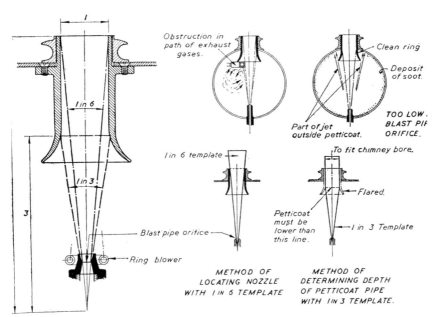

Fig. 59.—The setting of the blast pipe under chimney.

NOTE.—A double blast pipe and chimney to be set out in a like manner. (See Fig. 280, p. 244.) For a small model a single nozzle may be fitted, the exhaust steam being ejected through one orifice only, and the second orifice sealed. It is most important for steam to be exhausted equally from each orifice of both the manifold and chimney. Any diminution of steam from one or the other of the twin blast manifolds will tend to reduce smokebox vacuum. This will result in a serious loss of hot gases through the flue tubes, deadening of the fire in the grate and loss of steam pressure.

this. The alignment of the pipe can be made with the aid of a broach or rod with a centring disc fitted in the chimney. The position of the nozzle can then be determined with some degree of accuracy by the use of two cone templates as shown in Fig. 59. The effective length of the petticoat extension below the chimney is determined by the use of the "1 in 3" template. The "1 in 6" template fixes the position of the nozzle's throat in relation to the top of the chimney as shown.

It is very important to keep the exhaust passage clear of any internal fittings between nozzle and petticoat, otherwise the effectiveness of the blast is seriously impaired. A nozzle that is too low in the smokebox will not function properly since part of the gases will not be ejected. These will cause heavy deposits of soot.

In real practice the vacuum produced in the smokebox by the ejector action of the exhaust rises as high as 6 in. of water gauge, and it is this action that makes a locomotive boiler responsive in its rate of evaporation to the needs of the train. While the engine is stationary, the boiler may be doing no external work at all except in making up for the small losses by radiation; a few minutes later, due to the action of the exhaust in pulling on the fire, it may be developing its maximum horse-power, according to the weight of the train, speed and gradients.

Short funnels, common to modern locomotives, are usually extended inside the smokebox. To help steam raising the use of the petticoat pipe is often adopted. This allows the gases to leave the upper part of the smokebox easily.

In locomotives where a very high smokebox vacuum is not required, the intensity of the blast may be reduced by raising the nozzle in the smokebox.

Strength of Boilers

For a given thickness of material and diameter a plain cylindrical boiler made from solid drawn tube is, of course, the strongest of any—omitting reference to the flash boiler—and it is in this respect that the water-tube boiler is so satisfactory. The water-tube boiler has very few joints, and these can generally be hard soldered or brazed. A table of suitable steam pressures is given opposite.

When a cylindrical shell is made from sheet material, rolled into shape with a longitudinal joint, the strength of the boiler will depend on the efficiency of this joint. A single-riveted lap joint may only be 50% of the strength of the solid material, and a double-riveted joint about 75%. Flat end plates should be made of material not less than $1\frac{1}{4}$ times the thickness of the shell plates. All flat surfaces must be stayed. In using non-ferrous metals it should be noted that copper has diminished strength at high temperatures. The same applies to brass with the additional uncertainty as to the stability of the particular alloy one may be dealing with.

TABLE VII

RANGE OF STEAM PRESSURE

Gauge inches	Boiler Pressures lb. sq. in. (Gauge)	Temperature of Saturated Steam Degrees F.
$1\frac{3}{4}$	25 — 40	267 — 287
$2\frac{1}{4}$	35 — 50	280 — 297
$3\frac{1}{2}$	40 — 70	287 — 316
5	60 — 80	307 — 323
$7\frac{1}{4}$	60 — 90	307 — 331
$9\frac{1}{2}$	80 — 110	323 — 344
$10\frac{1}{4}$	80 — 110	323 — 344
15	120 — 180	350 — 380

The following formulæ may be used for estimating the working pressure for boilers:

$$WP = \frac{S \times P \times 2 \times R \times C \times T}{D \times F}$$

Where

S = Ultimate strength of the material in pounds per square inch.

viz.: Steel 63,000 lb.

Copper. 16,000 lb

Note:—Reference should be made to the appropriate B.S. Specifications for particulars of the materials to be employed for construction.

P = Plate thickness in inches

WP = Working pressure in lb. per square inch

F = Factor of safety 6 to 10

[61]

R = Riveting allowance 0·5 for single riveting, 0·75 for double riveting
  0·8 welded, brazed or silver-soldered joint
D = Diameter of boiler barrel in inches.
C = Corrosion allowance, steel below ¼ in. = 0·5 to 0·8.
T = Temperature allowance. For Copper at 400° F., T = 0·7, and at 212° F., T = 0·87.

For a given diameter of boiler the plate thickness would be:

$$P = \frac{D \times WP \times F}{S \times 2 \times R \times C \times T}$$

For staying flat surfaces steel stays should not be loaded to more than from 5,000 lb. in small boilers to 7,000 lb. per square inch in large boilers. Copper stays should not be loaded above 3,500 lb. per square inch safe load. The following stay spacings may be considered as accepted practice:

Up to ¾-in. scale, copper boilers ¾ in. to 1 in. apart.
1-in. to 1½-in. scale, copper boilers 1 in. to 1½ in. apart.
1½-in. scale, steel boilers 1½ in. to 1⅝ in. apart.
2-in. scale, copper boilers 1¾ in. to 2 in. apart.
2-in. scale, steel boilers 2¼ in. to 3 in. apart.
3-in. scale, steel boilers 3½ in. to 4 in. apart.

Stays should be threaded with fine threads, B.A. or model pipe threads in small sizes and B.S.P. threads in larger models.

In small copper boilers rivets should be at least 1½ times the plate thickness in diameter. The pitch should not be more than 3½ to 4 times the diameter.

Brazed or hard-soldered joints need be riveted only sufficiently to hold the work together while soldering. With soft-soldered joints the joint must be sufficiently strong to resist the working stresses without reference to the solder, which has no value at high temperatures. Any joint which is soft soldered must be close fitting. The plastic stage of ordinary soft solder is very near to the temperature of steam at 100 lb. per square inch. The soft solder is only a caulking material, and is the most satisfactory method of caulking in copper boilers. Minor crevices in steel boilers "take up" automatically owing to corrosion. This is not the case with copper boilers of the locomotive type.

Firebox

The design of the firebox depends on the class of fuel to be burned. A badly proportioned firebox may give rise to thermal losses due to incomplete combustion. A fuel with high volatile matter requires a greater volume to grate area ratio. The ratio can be lowered for anthracite fuel.

The firebox volume should not be so great as to reduce the temperature of the gases entering the tubes. Conversely, unburnt gases will be carried away from too small a firebox. Compromise has generally to be effected for one thing to compensate for the deficiencies of another. A deep firebox can be made to overcome the difficulty of a limited grate area. To do equal work the fuel must be burnt at a given rate per unit area. Therefore, to maintain this rate and to avoid excessive firing, the grate is made deeper.

Combustion Chambers

The provision of a combustion chamber virtually increases the heating surface of the firebox. In full-size practice where extra long boilers are employed, the addition of an extended firebox shortens the length of the flue tubes. For the average model the firebox accounts for over 50% of the total heating surface. A higher proportion of the total heat is conducted to the water in this area owing to the much higher temperature of the fuel and gases. Only a fraction of the remaining heat is absorbed through the walls of the tubes whilst the remainder is carried away to the chimney. In addition, some of this heat is used for superheating. Care must therefore be taken to ensure that the front end of the boiler is not starved of heat. This is important as water is a poor conductor of heat and requires fairly equitable heat distribution for the efficient generation of steam.

Superheating

Steam generated in a boiler is not by any means a perfect gas. It is said to be "wet" when it carries with it a quantity of moisture. Wet steam causes greater calorific losses and condensation in cylinders. Steam is dry or saturated when it contains no particles of water or moisture in suspension. A degree of dryness can be effected by "wire drawing." The term is used to define the process of throttling the steam supply at some point in its passage to the cylinders. The regulator is sometimes employed to advantage for this purpose.

The superheating of steam is accomplished by leading the steam pipes through the flue tubes *en route* to the cylinders. Further heat is thereby given up by the flue gases to some purpose. The superheated steam is elevated in temperature, is expanded to a proportionately greater volume but the pressure remains constant. For example, the normal temperature of steam at 100 lb. sq. in. is 338° F. By heating the steam to say 438° F. the degree of superheat added is simply the difference of the two temperatures, viz.: 100° F. (For saturated steam to reach a temperature of 438° F. the boiler pressure would have to be increased to 355 lb. sq. in.) Furthermore, the quantity of steam available, due to its expansion under this elevated temperature is increased by about 15%. These facts explain to some extent why an engine, if fitted with oversize cylinders can be made to work successfully without draining its boiler unduly.

As a guide, the ratio of superheater surface area to grate area is of the order of 10 to 1.

Flash or Coil Generators

The flash boiler is seldom employed in locomotive work as the degree of reliability is not great. In place of the orthodox boiler shell, a closely coiled length of steam pipe is enclosed in an insulated cylindrical casing. The coil is located directly over the firebox and the hot flue gases pass over the coil to the smokebox.

In the balance-tank system, the water supply is stored in a pressure vessel usually fitted in the tender. The water is fed via a check valve and safety valve to a primary coil in the firebox where it is flashed into saturated steam. From this point the steam supply is controlled by a regulator before passing through secondary coils to the cylinders.

The pressure of the feed water is maintained by an adequate supply of compressed air. The degree of superheat in this type of generator can be very high, therefore, all steam pipes and fittings and cylinders should be of ferrous materials. The moderate heat of a slow combustion coke or anthracite fire is recommended.

[64]

CHAPTER V
FRAMES, AXLEBOXES AND SPRINGS

THE construction of a model locomotive is a task often lightly entered upon and just as often laid aside uncompleted. This being the case, amateurs working in their spare time should consider the design they have chosen with a view to the amount of leisure they have at their disposal, as well as to the resources of their workshop. Where both are limited the best policy is to adopt a small type of locomotive in a comparatively large gauge rather than a smaller model of a large one. A design following no prototype will also be found less difficult. Strict adherence to every feature of a given prototype often causes a lot of extra work, although some may consider it well worth the trouble. Where the model engineer desires a reliable working model with the least possible labour he must be prepared to modify all details which are not visible or very noticeable from a normal point of view. The necessary alterations to the internal arrangement of boilers have already been discussed. Similarly cylinders and motion must be modified. In the matter of frames, so long

(Photo: K. N. Harris, Esq.)

Fig. 60.—Assembly stage of the main frames for the 5-in. gauge 0-4-4 tank locomotive "Henry Greenly" (built by the Kodak Model Engineering Society).

F

as the external shape is preserved, the components may be simplified in many ways.

In the earlier types of locomotives the main frames were constructed of hardwood timbers stiffened on each side with sheet iron plates. This method was superseded by inner and outer frames, thus forming what are known as "double" frames. (Fig. 15.)

TABLE VIII

THICKNESS OF FRAMES

Loco Gauge in.	Thickness in inches	I.S.G. No.
$1\frac{3}{4}$	$0 \cdot 05$	18
$2\frac{1}{2}$	$\frac{1}{16}$ or $\frac{5}{64}$	16 or 14
$3\frac{1}{2}$	$\frac{5}{64}$ or $\frac{3}{32}$	14 or 12
5	$\frac{1}{8}$ or $\frac{5}{32}$	10 or 8
$7\frac{1}{4}$	$\frac{3}{16}$	—
$9\frac{1}{2}$	$\frac{3}{16}$ or $\frac{1}{4}$	—
$10\frac{1}{4}$	$\frac{1}{4}$ or $\frac{5}{16}$	—
15	$\frac{1}{2}$ to $\frac{5}{8}$	—

Framing

All frames should be made of sheet metal. The thickness of the sheet used should be approximately a scale equivalent of $1\frac{1}{4}$ in. or $1\frac{1}{2}$ in., and conform approximately to the dimensions given in Table VIII.

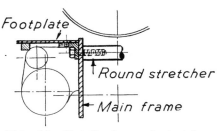

Fig. 61.—Detail of round stretcher bar with screwed-on brackets for the footplates.

American locomotives have forged bar frames measuring approximately 3 in. thick, and therefore if the bar type of frame is modelled out of sheet material then double the normal thickness will be required.

As far as possible the builder should avoid the use of tapped holes in the frames. Holes should be drilled and reamed for the bolts and screws attaching the stretchers, brackets and other parts.

[66]

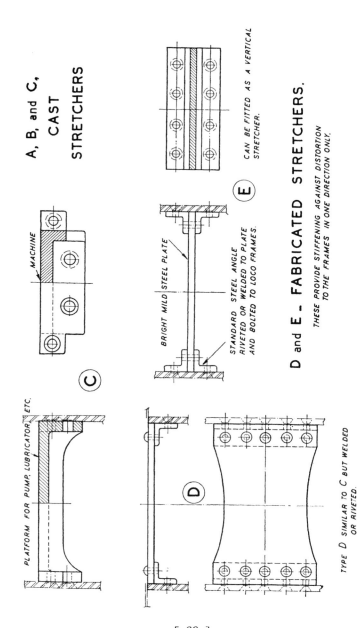

A, B, and C,
CAST
STRETCHERS

MACHINE

C

PLATFORM FOR PUMP, LUBRICATOR, ETC.

BRIGHT MILD STEEL PLATE

STANDARD STEEL ANGLE
RIVETED OR WELDED TO PLATE
AND BOLTED TO LOCO FRAMES.

CAN BE FITTED AS A VERTICAL
STRETCHER.

E

D and E – FABRICATED STRETCHERS.

THESE PROVIDE STIFFENING AGAINST DISTORTION
TO THE FRAMES IN ONE DIRECTION ONLY.

D

TYPE D SIMILAR TO C BUT WELDED
OR RIVETED.

Fig. 62.—Various types of locomotive frame stretchers.

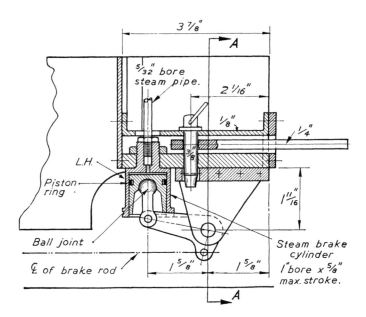

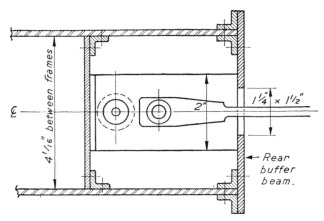

Fig. 63.—Arrangement of drag plate for 5-in. gauge British "Austerity" locomotive (2-8-0).

[70]

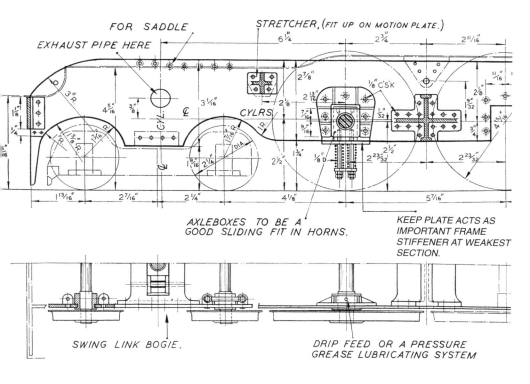

FOR SADDLE

EXHAUST PIPE HERE

STRETCHER, (FIT UP ON MOTION PLATE.)

CYL.

CYLRS

AXLEBOXES TO BE A
GOOD SLIDING FIT IN HORNS.

KEEP PLATE ACTS AS
IMPORTANT FRAME
STIFFENER AT WEAKEST
SECTION.

SWING LINK BOGIE.

DRIP FEED OR A PRESSURE
GREASE LUBRICATING SYSTEM

f. p. 70

Fig. 64A - Main Locomotive frames for 3½" gauge L.N.E.R. Pacific

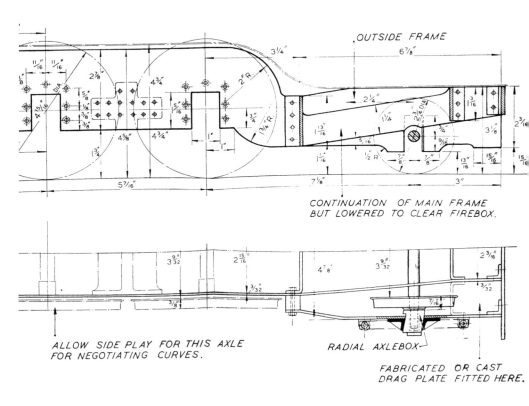

Fig. 64B - Main Locomotive frames for 3 1/2" gauge L.N.E.R. Pacific

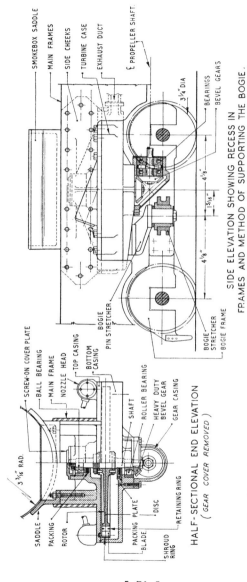

SMOKEBOX SADDLE
MAIN FRAMES
SIDE CHEEKS
TURBINE CASE
EXHAUST DUCT
℄ PROPELLER SHAFT

3¼" DIA
BEARINGS
BEVEL GEARS
4⅛"
5⁵⁄₁₆"
4⅛"

BOGIE
PIN STRETCHER
BOGIE
STRETCHER
BOGIE FRAME

SIDE ELEVATION SHOWING RECESS IN
FRAMES AND METHOD OF SUPPORTING THE BOGIE.

SCREW-ON COVER PLATE
BALL BEARING
MAIN FRAME
NOZZLE HEAD
TOP CASING
BOTTOM
CASING
SHAFT
ROLLER BEARING
HEAVY DUTY
BEVEL GEAR
GEAR CASING

3⁵⁄₁₆" RAD.

SADDLE
PACKING
ROTOR
PACKING PLATE
BLADE
DISC
RETAINING RING
SHROUD
RING

HALF-SECTIONAL END ELEVATION
(GEAR COVER REMOVED)

Fig. 64a.—Design for turbine power unit mounted in main frames directly over bogie.
5-in. gauge, 1/11 scale.

Auxiliary or Outside Frames

A practical example of the use of auxiliary frames is shown in the author's free-lance design, Fig. 45 (*b*). Here the rear frame is set outside the main frame, the latter extending forward only as far as the boiler throat plate, thereby allowing the fitting of a wide firebox.

An example is illustrated in Fig. 64 (facing p. 86). In this case the main frames extend the whole length of the locomotive and are curved downwards to the rear in order to clear the firebox above. The outer frames are set outside the firebox and carry the radial axlebox and trailing wheels.

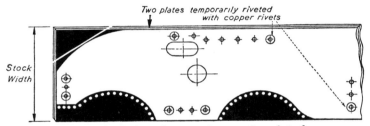

Fig. 65.—Method of cutting-out locomotive plate frames.

A similar form is employed on L.M.S. locomotives except that a trailing pony truck is employed in place of a radial axlebox. (Fig. 65a.)

As a rule the buffer planks are fixed to the main frames by rolled steel angles. Castings are largely employed for the smaller gauge models (Fig. 67), being cast with an upper platform and with lugs for securing the main framing. These lugs are milled to suit the thickness of the frame plating and one or two bolts or screws in each lug serve to secure the whole structure. The table top of these castings can be used to fix footplates and other fittings.

Axle Bearings

Spring-loaded axleboxes can be fitted to miniature cast gunmetal horn-blocks for No. 1 (1¾ in.) gauge. The horns should be carefully machined (Fig. 68) aligned and bolted to the slotted frames. The gunmetal axleboxes, which must be a good sliding fit in the horns, are slung on a single coil spring. Provision

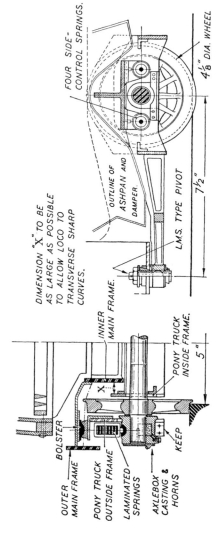

FOUR SIDE-CONTROL SPRINGS.

$4\frac{1}{8}''$ DIA. WHEEL

OUTLINE OF ASHPAN AND DAMPER.

L.M.S. TYPE PIVOT

$7\frac{1}{2}''$

DIMENSION "X" TO BE AS LARGE AS POSSIBLE TO ALLOW LOCO TO TRANSVERSE SHARP CURVES.

INNER MAIN FRAME.

5"

PONY TRUCK INSIDE FRAME.

X

BOLSTER

OUTER MAIN FRAME

PONY TRUCK OUTSIDE FRAME

LAMINATED SPRINGS

AXLEBOX CASTING & HORNS

KEEP

Fig. 65a.—Assembly of L.M.R. type trailing pony truck for 5-in. gauge model.

[73]

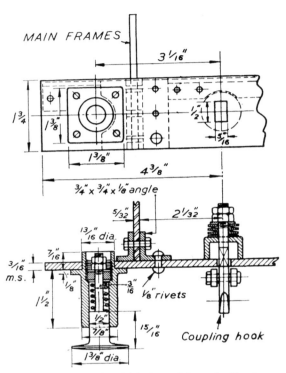

Fig. 66.—Assembly of fabricated front buffer-beam.

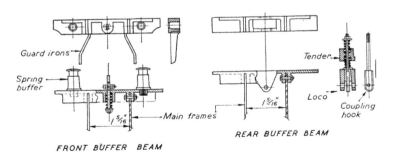

FRONT BUFFER BEAM

REAR BUFFER BEAM

Fig. 67.—Front and rear buffer beams for No. 1 gauge model

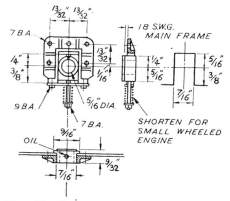

Fig. 68.—Locomotive horns and axlebox for No. 1 gauge model.

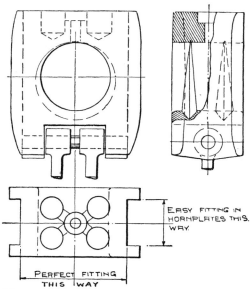

Fig. 69.—Details of axlebox for 9½-in. gauge
locomotive.

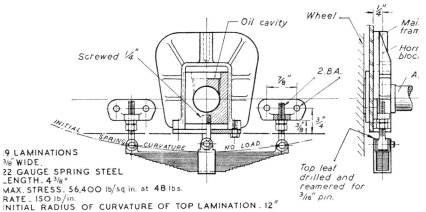

Oil cavity

Wheel

Screwed 1/4"

2.B.A.

7/8"

INITIAL SPRING CURVATURE NO LOAD

Mai frame

Horn bloc.

A.

3/8" 3/4"

9 LAMINATIONS
3/8" WIDE.
22 GAUGE SPRING STEEL
LENGTH. 4 3/8"
MAX. STRESS. 56,400 lb/sq.in. at 48 lbs.
RATE. 150 lb/in.
INITIAL RADIUS OF CURVATURE OF TOP LAMINATION. 12"

Top leaf
drilled and
reamered for
3/16" pin.

Fig. 70a.—Assembly of laminated springs for "Royal Scot" locomotive.

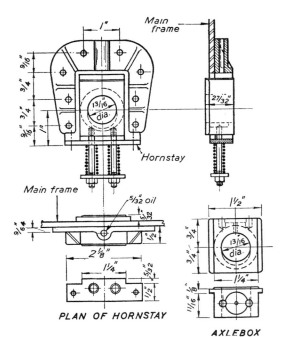

1"

Main frame

9/16"
3/4"
3/4"
9/16"
1"

13/16" dia.

Hornstay

27/32"

Main frame

5/32 oil
5/32
9/16"
1/2"
2 1/8"
1 1/4"
1/2"

1 1/2"
3/4"
13/16" dia.
3/4"
1 1/4"
11/16" 1/8"

PLAN OF HORNSTAY

AXLEBOX

Fig. 70.—Locomotive cast horn and axlebox for 5-in. gauge model.

[76]

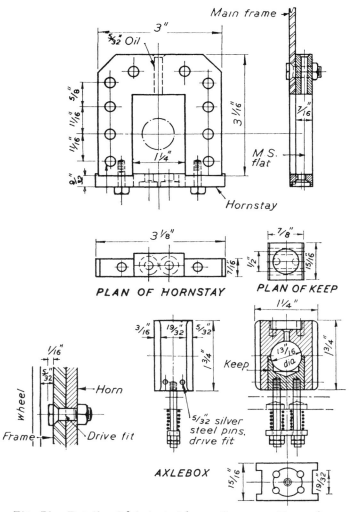

Fig. 71.—Details of fabricated horns for assembly on frames in
lieu of castings (5-in. gauge).

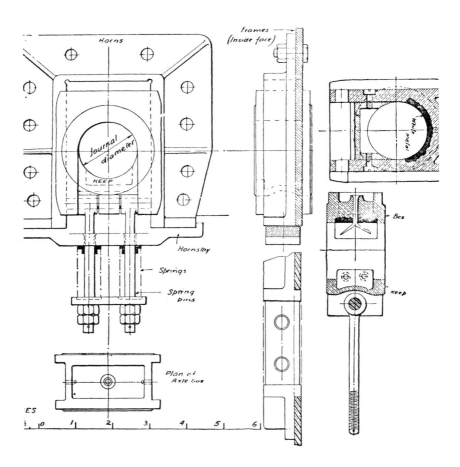

Fig. 71a.—Design of axlebox for a small 15-in. gauge locomotive.

is also made to lubricate the journals. A standard combined stretcher and hornblock (Fig. 62) is an excellent arrangement where there are no eccentrics fitted to the axle, especially in the region of the firebox where the axle requires protection against overheating.

In fitting any spring-borne axlebox the box should not be too rigid a fit laterally. It is always better to have some side play to allow the axlebox to tip slightly as it rises and falls.

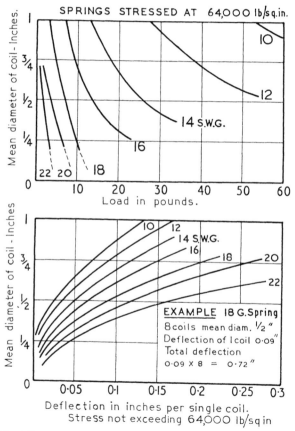

Fig. 72.—Graphs for determining the sizes of springs.

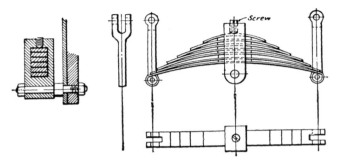

Fig. 73.—Details of packed laminated springs for bearings.

No play, however, must be allowed in a fore-and-aft direction other than that absolutely necessary to easy working.

Other Forms of Axleboxes

For larger locomotives axleboxes made as shown in Fig. 69 are used. The length of such a bearing should be equal to the diameter. This type of axlebox may be made from a gun metal casting, the eccentric groove being formed by a pointed boring tool in the lathe. Unless a separate keep is provided, as in the case of the axlebox shown in Fig. 71a, the box must be placed on the axles before the wheels, and when once in place cannot be removed. The design shown in the last illustration is practically the same as that used in a real locomotive.

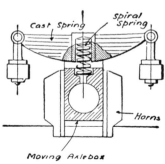

Fig. 74.—Cast "dummy" spring with spiral spring concealed in the buckle.

Spiral Springs

Spiral springs are largely used in working model locomotives, and to determine the correct size of spring required for a given load the diagram (Fig. 72) may be employed. If the load be 5 lb., and a suitable deflection $\frac{1}{8}$ in. with a 10-coil spring, one with a mean diameter (D) of 0·6 in. with 18 s.w.G. wire will provide this deflection as shown on the deflection diagram. Referring to the safe-load diagram, it will be found that for 5 lb. an 18 s.w.g. spring 0·6 in. diameter is quite safe. It is obvious that a finer gauge wire, say 20G., would not be suitable as in 0·6 in. diameter it is only safe up to 2 lb. load. The number of coils does not affect the safe load, only the deflection. The diagrams suit both compression and tension springs.

Laminated Springs

It may be taken as an axiom that laminated springs, if made to scale, will have little or no deflection, certainly not sufficient for the purpose of a working model. Where, for the

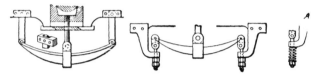

Fig. 75.—Examples of suspended laminated springs.

sake of external appearance, they must be employed, then one of two methods must be adopted. As shown in Fig. 73, spring-steel plates are used (clock springs make excellent leaves), and to reduce the stiffness the plates are packed out with strips of brass or soft steel placed in the centre. This gives the required "bulk" to the spring and at the same time provides sufficient resiliency. The other method is to cast the "springs" in the solid and to use spiral springs concealed in the buckle (Fig. 74) or in the suspension links as indicated at A (Fig. 75), and in the arrangement of bogie shown in Fig. 101. The only difficulty in using plate springs is the eye-end of the largest (or back) plate. Usually this is chosen out of thicker stuff than the remainder, and the eye is a piece of tube or drilled steel rod brazed on. Some skill is required to temper the plate at the same time. The drawings in Fig. 75 show various suspensions for laminated springs. In modern model engineering practice the real laminated spring in working order is favoured, and to this end the design in Fig. 70a has been prepared.

CHAPTER VI

WHEELS, AXLES, CRANK AXLES, AND CRANK PINS

Types of Wheels

LOCOMOTIVE wheels are of three types: (a) driving wheels, (b) coupled wheels, and (c) carrying wheels, and except for the disposition of balance weights there is little difference between the first two types. In actual practice wheels are made in two parts, the centres being of wrought or cast steel, or sometimes cast iron, and the tyres of a good quality hard steel, such as Bessemer steel. The tyres are shrunk on and fastened by studs or by retaining rings. Only in the largest models carrying passengers are separate tyres employed. Wheels are for the most part flanged; in eight- or ten-coupled engines one pair of wheels may have flangeless tyres to assist in negotiating sharp curves. Wheels are fixed to the axles by shrinking or forcing and securing by keys. In model practice one-piece cast-iron wheels are usually employed, although there are exceptions whereby wheels are made with separate steel tyres even for the smaller-scale locomotives. Furthermore, wheels have also been turned from the solid steel bar; the space between spokes drilled out and the spokes finished off true-to-scale by hand-filing throughout

(Photo: K. N. Harris, Esq.)

Fig. 76.—Assembly of wheels and frames for the 5-in. gauge tank locomotive "Henry Greenly." (See Fig. 60.)

Fig. 77.—Assembly of locomotive horns and
axleboxes for No. 1 gauge models.

The Number of Spokes

The following table gives particulars of the numbers of
spokes usual in real and in model wheels of various scales. It
will readily be understood that it would be difficult to mould
a wheel casting to, say, $\frac{1}{2}$ in. to the foot or smaller exactly to
scale.

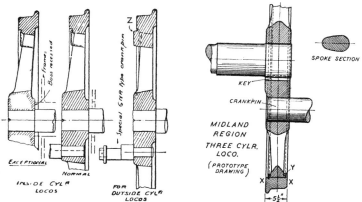

Fig. 78.—Typical sections through driving wheels.

TABLE IX

NUMBER OF WHEEL SPOKES

	Full-size	$\frac{3}{4}$ in. scale and larger	$2\frac{1}{2}$ in. gauge	$1\frac{3}{4}$ in. gauge
Bogie Wheels				
3 ft. to 3 ft. 6 in. ..	10	10	10	8 to 10
Carrying and Tender Wheels				
3 ft. 6 in. to 4 ft. 6 in.	12 to 14	12 to 14	12	10 to 12
Shunting Engine Coupled				
4 ft. to 4 ft. 9 in. ..	13 to 14	14	12 or 13	12
Tank Engine Coupled				
5 ft. to 5 ft. 6 in. ..	16 to 18	16 to 18	14 to 16	13 to 15
Passenger Engine Coupled				
6 ft. to 6 ft. 9 in. ..	18 to 22	18 to 22	17 to 20	16 to 18
7 ft. to 7 ft. 9 in. ..	22 to 24	22 to 24	20 to 22	18 to 20

In a small working model there is no objection to an odd number of spokes if it will improve the appearance of the wheel by making it nearly to scale and at the same time practical from the point of view of the foundry.

The modern cast-steel wheel has spokes of oval section. This is not followed in small models, as moulding is rendered more difficult, and therefore a straight-sided section is employed. The taper should be adequate and regular.

The balance weights of the prototype may be copied exactly, and a balance equal to the original will be obtained if the same number of cylinders and cranks are employed. A diagram showing the usual types of wheels employed is included in Fig. 79, where C = coupled, ID = inside-cylinder driving, SD = single driving (outside-cylinder), T = tender or trailing, OD = outside-cylinder driving wheels, ISD = inside-cylinder driving, and SB = small bogie wheels. The cross sections of the wheels (Fig. 78) exemplify the types employed. For an inside-cylinder engine the face of the wheel is often coned outwards, so that the maximum length of axle-box journal can be obtained. This coning is accentuated in the case of the driving axle of several types of engines.

In modern outside-cylinder engines the face of the wheel spokes are usually quite flat, as the available width for the outside motion is limited. Balance weights, however, are

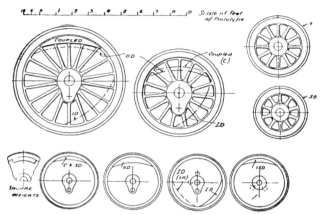

Fig. 79.—Types of Locomotive Wheels.

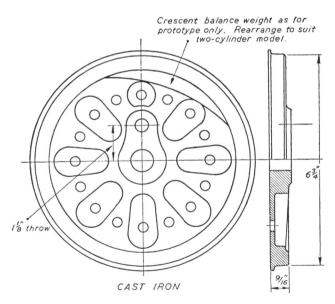

Crescent balance weight as for
prototype only. Rearrange to suit
two-cylinder model.

$1\frac{1}{8}''$ throw

CAST IRON

$6\frac{3}{4}''$

$9\frac{1}{16}''$

Fig. 80.—Simplified form of wheel for Southern Railway "Pacific"
type model locomotive.

[85]

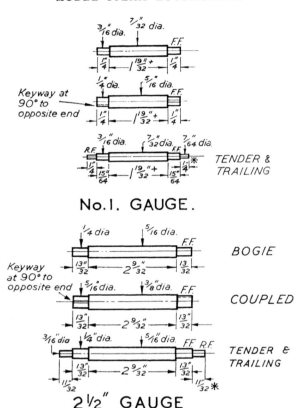

No.1. GAUGE.

2 1/2" GAUGE

Fig. 81.—Typical axles for No. 1, 2½-in. and 3½-in. gauge
locomotives and tenders (*denotes that the dimension is
variable and depends upon the design of the axlebox).

arranged to project beyond the face of the tyre, as in z, (Fig. 78)
so that the plane of these weights more nearly coincides with
the parts they are counterbalancing.

In full-size locomotive practice, engineers have developed
new types of wheels to meet improvements in design of other
parts of the engine mechanism. An outline of the type of wheel
fitted to S.R. "Merchant Navy" class locomotives is shown in
Fig. 80. The external features of the wheel can be followed in
a model given a good pattern from which castings can be made.

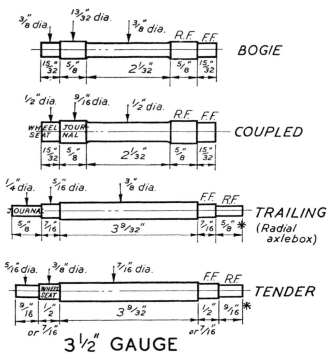

Fig. 81a.—Axles for No. 1, 2½-in. and 3½-in. gauge locomotives and tenders (*denotes that the dimension is variable and depends upon the design of the axlebox).

Patterns for Wheels

In making patterns the tyre and flange and the back of the wheel boss should be left much thicker than required; other parts may be finished sizes, allowance being made for shrinkage. One master wood pattern, with double shrinkage allowance, may be made for a set of coupled wheels, brass castings obtained, cleaned, and balance weights added in their respective positions and sizes. Wheels can always be repeated, and the character of the whole set is much easier to preserve than if separate patterns are attempted. The width of tyres for various scales are given in Table II. The average width in real practice is from 5¼ in. to 5⅝ in. with a depth of flange of about 1⅛ in. The angle of coning of the treads should not exceed 1 in 20, and

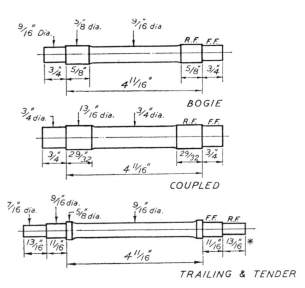

BOGIE

COUPLED

TRAILING & TENDER

5" GAUGE

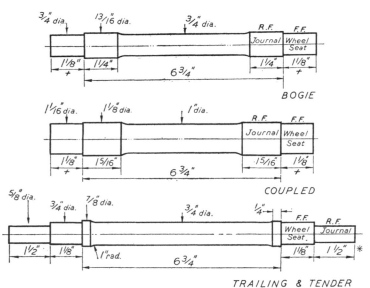

BOGIE

COUPLED

TRAILING & TENDER

7¼" GAUGE

Fig. 82.—Types of axles for 5-in. and 7¼-in. gauge model locomotives and tenders.

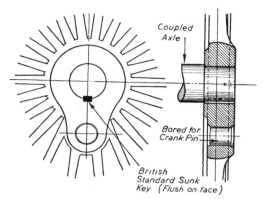

Fig. 83.—Detail of wheel centre for the 7¼-in. gauge "King" Class (G.W.R.) locomotive designed by the author.

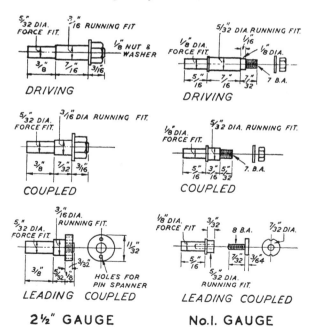

Fig. 84.—Details of crank pins for No. 1 and 2½-in. gauge models.

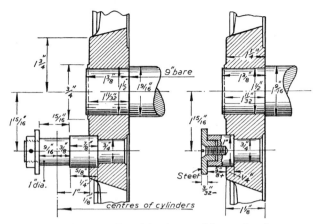

Fig. 85.—Details of large model crank pins.

the outer sharp arris should be turned off at an angle of 45°.
The face of the wheel marked y in the section (Fig. 78) should
not be turned but, to give a good result, should be quite true
and neat in the original pattern. Then the faces x only will need
machining.

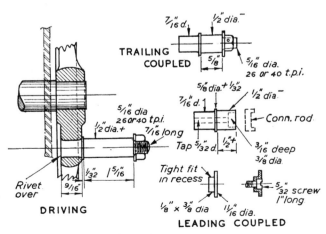

Fig. 86.—Details of crank pins for 5-in. gauge model.

[90]

Turning Wheels

In turning a wheel the casting should be fettled up, so that on chucking it by the tread, back outwards, it runs reasonably true. The edge of the flange may then be turned nearly to size (but parallel), the back of the wheel and boss being faced and the hole of the axle bored. Never drill small wheels from the face side. Gauges should be made so that all similar wheels have the same bore, at least within half to a quarter thousandth of an inch. The wheel may then be reversed in the chuck and finished off.

Axles

The axles of full-size locomotives are made of an acid open-hearth steel of a character which will stand shocks. They have collars next to the wheels and journals. These may be copied in the model, but reliance in larger working models should not be placed on such collars for taking lateral loads. The wheel - boss faces provide much better surfaces. The ordinary model axle is not sub-jected to such heavy stresses as in a real loco-motive, but wear and tear is greater on outdoor lines, due to the working parts being closer to the ground.

Fig. 81 shows typical axles for smaller gauge models, while Fig. 82 represents the author's practice for engines of 1 in. scale and larger. Axles should be forced into the wheels, the axles

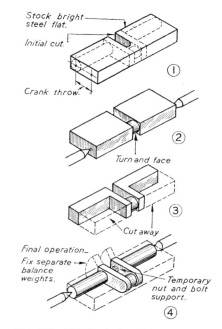

Fig. 87.—Method of making a single-throw crank axle from stock material (mild steel) for a simple model.

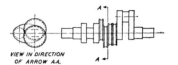

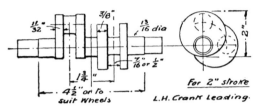

VIEW IN DIRECTION
OF ARROW A.A.

Fig. 88.—Detail of a two-throw crank axle for model Caledonian Railway 4-4-0 locomotive. The axle is fitted with two sets of eccentric sheaves for Stephenson's valve gear.

Fig. 89.—Worsdell type of crank axle for small model.

being from $\frac{1}{2}$ to $1\frac{1}{2}$ thousandth larger than the hole according to the size of the axle. The increase in size should be slightly greater at the back than at the front, but this does not mean that the fitting at the latter point should in any way be loose. Centres should always be left in the axles so that wheels may be skimmed true. The distance between tyres is so important that accuracy must be observed in all lateral dimensions of wheels and axles.

Bogie and carrying wheels require no fixing other than that provided by the force fitting, but driving and coupled wheels must be secured by pins or keys. A satisfactory method is a screw or parallel pin driven axially half in the wheel and half in the shaft. Screwing wheels on to the axle is bad practice.

The maximum length of journal possible should be obtained. This will vary from $\frac{1}{4}$-in. long in small engines to $1\frac{1}{4}$ times the

Fig. 90.—Crank axle with oval webs and eccentrics machined from solid bar.

diameter in larger models. Crank-pins or crank axles should never be less than two-thirds the diameter of the axle in length.

Crank Pins

Crank pins are an item in model locomotive construction which depend for design on the size of the engine.

For No. 1 gauge engines the designs shown in Fig. 84 are adopted, while for larger engines Fig. 85 is representative. Modern outside-cylinder locomotives often have very small clearances between the connecting rods and leading coupling

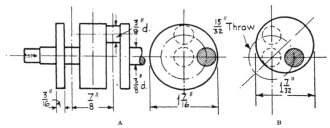

Fig. 91.—Alternative forms of simple two-throw crank axle.

Fig. 92.—Crank axle with slip eccentric sheaves.

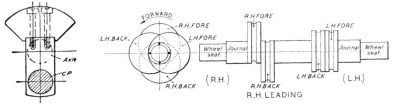

Fig. 93.—Method of counterbalancing a crank axle for a small model with built-up webs.

Fig. 94.—Eccentric sheaves solid with axle. (For Stephenson's link motion.)

rod crank pins. This leads to special arrangements for retaining the rods. (Fig. 86.) The retaining caps should fit the cranks tightly, so that the screw has little work to do in holding it in place. (For model work the three-screw method is the least satisfactory.)

Where screwed-on retaining nuts or collars, such as are shown in Fig. 85 are used, the addition of a pin is essential. Changes in diameter of crank pins (and axles) should be protected from failure by corners of ample 'radii, this being very important in large working models.

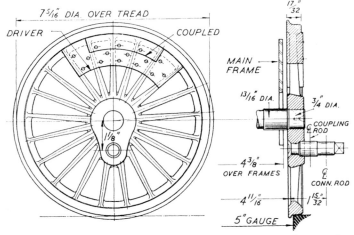

Fig. 95.—Detail of coupled wheel for 5-in. gauge locomotive.

Special crank pins are used on the G.N.R. "Atlantics" (see Fig. 78), which provide different throws for the connecting rod and coupling rod respectively.

Crank Axles

These are indigenous to Great Britain. In America and abroad generally outside cylinder locomotives are the rule. In France, however, quite a large number of cranked axles are employed on four-cylinder compounds.

A simple single-throw crank axle can be turned in the

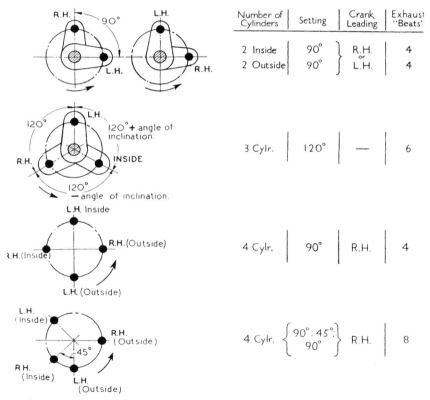

Number of Cylinders	Setting	Crank Leading	Exhaust "Beats"
2 Inside	90°	R.H. or L.H.	4
2 Outside	90°		4
3 Cylr.	120°	—	6
4 Cylr.	90°	R.H.	4
4 Cylr.	90°:45° / 90°	R.H.	8

Fig. 96.—Crank-setting diagram for two-, three- and four-cylinder locomotives.

(*Photo: "The Model Engineer"*)

Fig. 97.—Assembly of wheels and built-up crank axle for model of the original G.W.R. broad-gauge locomotive "North Star". Made by K. N. Harris, Esq.

lathe from round mild steel stock material of a diameter that will include the webs of the crank. (Fig. 87.)

(*Photo: "The Model Engineer"*)

Fig. 97a.—Wheels and built-up balanced crank axle for 5 in. gauge locomotive.

Oval crank webs are often made for locomotive work and Fig. 88 shows the arrangement of the crank axle complete with the eccentrics for a $3\frac{1}{2}$-in. gauge Caledonian Railway express locomotive. In order to turn in the lathe the axle itself, crank pins and the various eccentric sheaves, the stock bar or forging must be centred accordingly. In this particular case there are no less than seven points to be marked off at each end respectively.

No advantage would appear to accrue by making a large model crank on the built-up method, but where balance webs are required—because of their use in the particular prototype being modelled—these can be made separately and applied to the webs of the crank axle.

The position of the cylinders and the type of valve gear used will largely determine the proportions of a crank axle. Where space is limited, the use of round webs—the thickness of which may be half that of the crank diameter—will be found quite satisfactory. Fig. 91 (A) shows a type of axle with a single central web which can be machined with the least trouble. More metal must be removed than is necessary where the webs are twisted to 90°, but where the tools are available this part of the work may be relegated to a heavy roughing lathe. The setting out shown at B represents another solution of the problem. In small models having slip eccentrics the crank webs can very often be utilized as stops for the shifting eccentric sheaves in their two positions. This device is shown in Fig. 92. Nearly all engines with outside cylinders and link motion, designed by the writer over a period of years, have had the eccentrics solid with the driving axle. On the whole much labour is saved, a sound job results, and much smaller sheaves than otherwise possible can be obtained. Fig. 90 is a typical example of this practice, whilst Fig. 94 shows a set of link-motion eccentrics solid with a plain axle as used for outside-cylinder locomotives.

The diagram Fig. 93 shows a method of applying counter-weights to the rectangular webs of a crank axle, which could be used in modelling some types of L.S.W.R. inside-cylinder locomotives.

Some typical designs of wheels and axles are shown in Figs. 95 and 97. Special attention must be given to the fitting of the return cranks for locomotives employing either Walschaerts' or Baker valve gear.

Fig. 96 shows the various crank settings for two-, three- and four-cylinder locomotives. It should be noted that for three- and four-cylinder schemes the inside cylinders usually drive the leading coupled axle and the outside cylinders drive the second pair of coupled wheels. In cases where all cylinders drive on to the second pair of coupled wheels, the inside cylinders must be inclined for the motion to clear the leading coupled axle. The crank settings must be adjusted accordingly.

H

CHAPTER VII

BOGIES, PONY TRUCKS AND RADIAL AXLEBOXES

Bogies

A BOGIE is a separate carriage or truck attached to and supporting the main frame of the locomotive by a central pivot or "bogie pin." It is usually carried on four wheels of relatively small diameter and provides the necessary support for the front or rear end of the engine in a manner which renders the whole wheel base of the locomotive more flexible on curves than if the frames were carried on rigid axles. As a rule, a four-wheeled bogie is much to be preferred to a two-wheeled truck or any

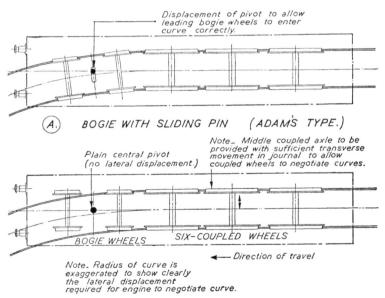

Displacement of pivot to allow leading bogie wheels to enter curve correctly.

(A.) *BOGIE WITH SLIDING PIN (ADAM'S TYPE.)*

Note. Middle coupled axle to be provided with sufficient transverse movement in journal to allow coupled wheels to negotiate curves.

Plain central pivot (no lateral displacement.)

BOGIE WHEELS *SIX-COUPLED WHEELS*

←— *Direction of travel*

Note. Radius of curve is exaggerated to show clearly the lateral displacement required for engine to negotiate curve.

(B) *BOGIE WITHOUT A SLIDE CANNOT FOLLOW TRACK.*

[98]

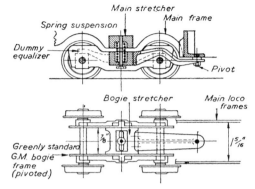

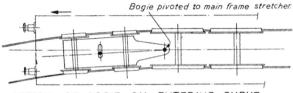

MODEL BISSEL BOGIE ADAPTED FOR No.I. GAUGE.

Bogie pivoted to main frame stretcher.

ACTION OF BOGIE ON ENTERING CURVE.

Fig. 99.—The action of the Bissel type bogie on a curved track.

Fig. 100.—Adam's type of bogie for $7\frac{1}{4}$-in. gauge model of G.C.R. locomotive.

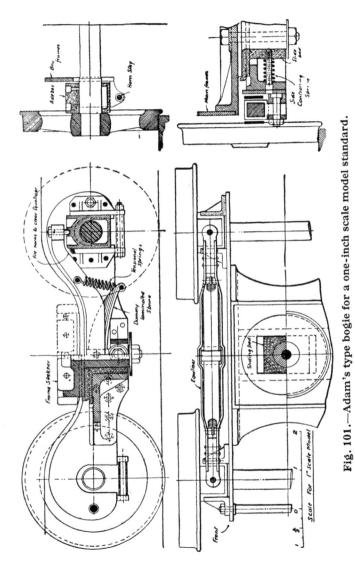

Fig. 101.—Adam's type bogie for a one-inch scale model standard.

other form of radial axle at the leading end of an express locomotive. A bogie also fits very conveniently below the cylinders.

In real practice the length of the wheel-base ranges from 75 in. to 102 in. The bogie pin is usually placed on the centre line of the wheel base. In order to effect a more equitable weight distribution on the respective axles, however, the bogie pin is sometimes moved slightly to the rear. More weight is therefore brought to bear on the rear axle than on the front axle.

A four-wheeled bogie on a fixed central pivot does not

Fig. 102.—Assembly of No. 1 gauge bogie castings and finished parts.

function correctly on curved track. The bogie in such a locomotive must slide laterally as well as turn on its pivot, as shown at A (Fig. 98). It is also desirable that the sliding box or pad piece into which the bogie pin fits should be controlled by springs or some equivalent device which will tend to keep the truck central. This is most important in larger models carrying passengers in order to prevent the bogie end of the locomotive "nosing" from side to side when travelling on a straight track.

For the Bissell type of bogie (Fig. 99), the pivot is placed behind the rear bogie wheel, so that the centre of the truck virtually slides and turns on a radius. Its action is only truly correct for one particular radius of curve, and therefore is considered objectionable in full-size work. It is, however, for a model a very simple form of construction, easily controlled

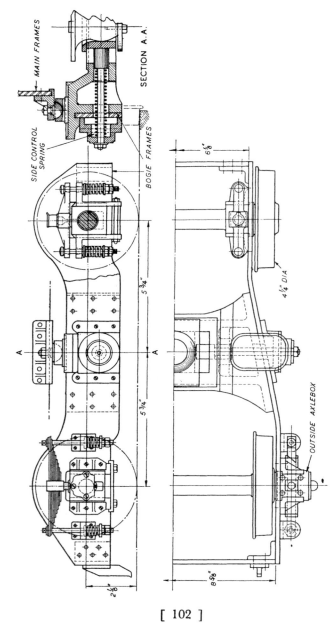

MAIN FRAMES

SECTION A.A.

SIDE CONTROL SPRING

BOGIE FRAMES

OUTSIDE AXLEBOX

Fig. 103.—Arrangement of bogie for 7¼-in. gauge model of "King George V", No. 6,000, 4-6-0 (G.W.R.).

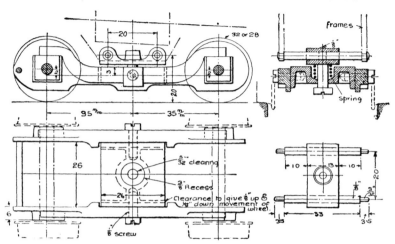

Fig. 104.—Bogie with equalizing frames and central spring for No. 1 gauge model.

and works quite well in practice. As illustrated, it is suitable for small gauge models. The frames act as equalizers, being pivoted to the cross plate. A central post with a spring should be fitted to a convenient frame stretcher to limit its movement and provide for vertical springing of the bogie.

Examples of "Adams," or sliding pivot bogies, common to British locomotives are illustrated in Figs. 100 and 101. The bogie (Fig. 101) has frames set at a narrower distance apart than those of the locomotive, so that an equalizer and spring may be applied to both axleboxes on each side. The bogie

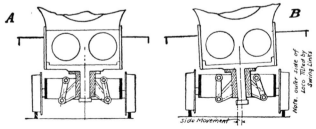

Fig. 105.—Diagram illustrating the action of swing-links.

Fig. 106.—Underside of a swing-link type of bogie.

(Photo: K. N. Harris, Esq.)

Fig. 106a.—Assembly of swing link bogie.

frames are connected by a central stretcher casting, and a pad piece is located in a slot in this stretcher and is free to slide laterally. The circular top flange of this pad supports the weight of the front end of the locomotive. The pad is also bored to take the pin. This pin is fixed to or is part of the stretcher secured to the main frames of the locomotive. The sliding block is fitted with spiral or laminated side-controlling springs which tend to keep it central. No control of the swivelling movement of the bogie on the pin is usual or necessary.

The Adams type of bogie is very simply modelled in small scales by slotting the cross stretcher to take the pin, the sliding block being omitted. Side control is only essential in any engine of the smaller gauges in which the centre of the rigid wheel base is some distance from the bogie centre, as, for instance, in a 0–4–4 or 2–6–4 type model. The slot in small models should be as wide as possible, as curves are proportionately much sharper than in large examples. A modification of the sliding type of bogie suitable for $1\frac{3}{4}$-in, gauge is provided for by a sliding block fitted to two round rods bolted to the main frames (Fig. 104). The bogie pin is a shouldered screw, while the springing of the whole truck is effected by a single central spring. The frames of the bogie act as an equalizer, so that the whole of the functions of the orthodox type of locomotive bogie (as in Fig. 101) are preserved. It is important to note that equalizing the side frames on a pivot alone is not sufficient. The central spring allows for a complete rise and fall of one side or the other of the bogie truck, a feature which an uneven road surface demands. The round rods with shouldered ends make a very simple frame stretcher.

The swing-link bogie is not often employed in modern practice but may prove serviceable for small models. The usual sliding block is employed, but this block does not bear directly on the cross stretcher of the bogie. The block, and therefore the weight of the part of the engine the bogie supports, is connected to the bogie stretcher by a set of links placed at a slight inclination on each side as shown in the diagram, Fig. 105, at A. These links, due to the weight upon them, tend to maintain the bogie in the central position, as will be seen from the sketch B. Further, the outer rail of the curve tends to lift the engine, and therefore increases pressure on the outer wheels. This assists in preventing the flange from mounting the rail.

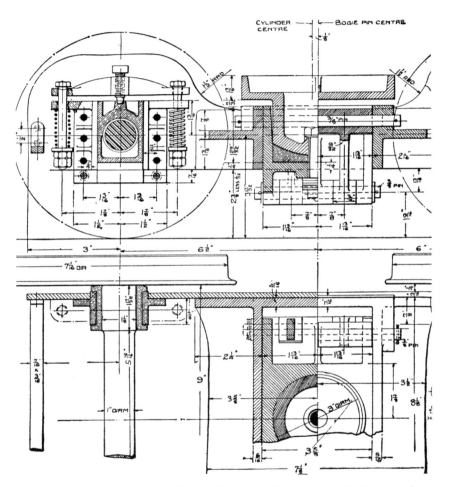

Fig. 107.—G.N.R. swing-link bogie for 2-in. scale model locomotive.

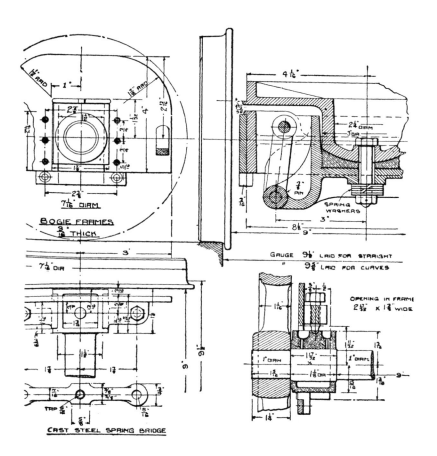

Fig. 107a.

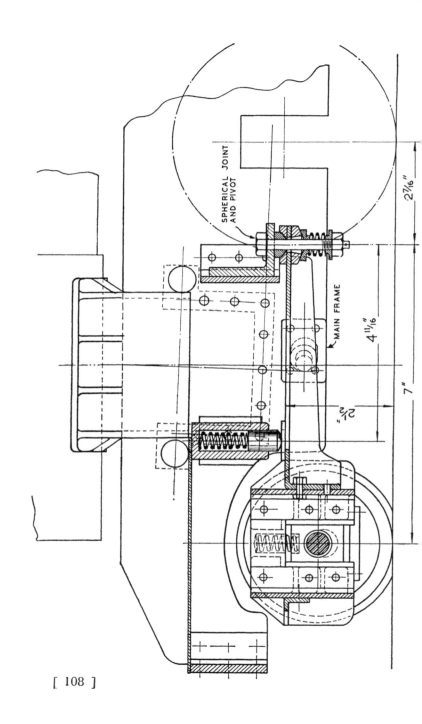

SPHERICAL JOINT AND PIVOT

MAIN FRAME

2⁷⁄₁₆″

4¹¹⁄₁₆″

7″

2¹⁄₂″

[108]

Fig. 111.—Model of the Maunsell pony truck as fitted to a S.E.C.R. 2–6–0 locomotive.

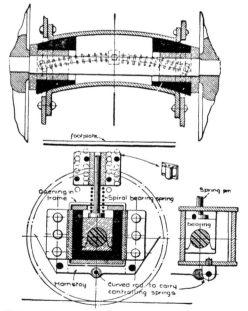

Fig. 112.—Radial axlebox for a large model.

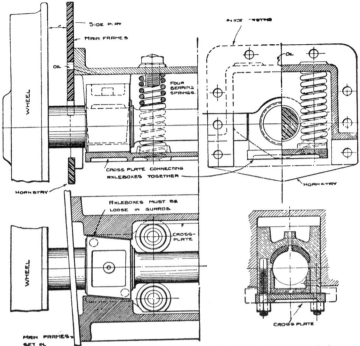

Fig. 113.—Radial axlebox for 3-in. scale 15-in. gauge miniature
locomotive.

Concealed Springs

As laminated springs are not of much use in a small model,
and, as they are fitted to equalizers to the exclusion of other
types of springs in actual practice, it is usual to devise some
method of concealing a spiral spring in the buckle of the dummy
model laminated spring or on the ends of the equalizer. Fig. 101
shows one method, while the various schemes for bearing springs
illustrated in Chapter V will suggest others. Where the imitation
of the laminated spring is not attempted, then spiral springs
may be used either underhung as shown in Fig. 109 at A or
overhung as at B. The first method has the disadvantage that
should the engine become derailed the spring pins are bound
to be bent or otherwise damaged. By placing the springs on
top of the equalizer no such damage is possible. Moreover, the
arrangement looks very neat and is quite effective.

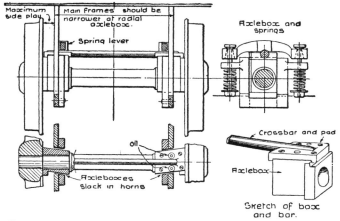

Fig. 114.—A simple arrangement for producing a radial movement to axleboxes in a small model.

Pony Trucks

The rear pony truck is to be preferred to the radial axlebox for its greater flexibility. The action on a curve is the same as that of the "Bissell" four-wheeled bogie; and similarly a truck of a given radius is only suitable for one particular curve. As only one pair of wheels is employed, this fault is of no great importance in practice. The radius of the truck should

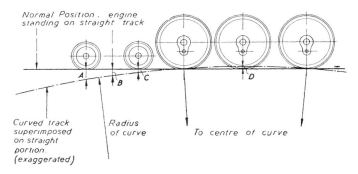

Fig. 115.—Diagram showing the displacement of locomotive wheels (4–6–0) on a curved track. (See additional typeset notes.)

Fig. 116.—Detail of bogie for model of the G.W.R. 4-2-2 locomotive "Majestic" (No. 3048).

be proportioned so that the axle is truly radial to the centre of the average curve.

Some form of side control is essential for models from $3\frac{1}{2}$-in. gauge, upwards.

Fig. 109 shows an arrangement of truck employed for a 1-inch scale model. The pivot is a universal joint, and the bearing springs are integral with the truck and stretcher casting. Fig. 110 shows an adaptation to the leading end of a No. 1 gauge locomotive

(Photo: K. N. Harris, Esq.)

Fig. 117.—Chassis of model "Pacific" locomotive under construction.

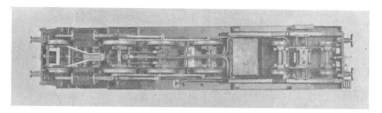

Fig. 118.—The underside of a model 2-6-4 tank locomotive showing the arrangement of the leading pony truck and rear bogie.

with outside cylinders, the frame stretcher being a special casting with lugs to suit.

It is important that main frames which are adjacent to bogie wheels or pony trucks should be reduced in width to provide for the required side play. In modern engines bogie and pony truck wheels are often made of relatively small diameter so that they can swing clear under the main frames. This is not always possible, and the limits prescribed by the presence of main frames bears to an important extent on the general design of the engine with respect to the minimum radius of curves that can be negotiated.

Radial Axleboxes

The action of the radial axlebox is identical with that of the pony truck such as just described. The axleboxes are usually inside the frames, are tied together and guided by inclined or curved horns. For the type of radial axlebox illustrated in Fig. 112 the sliding movement of the axlebox is entirely separate from the vertical motion of the wheels on the bearing springs. The radial axlebox (Fig. 113) is designed for a large model in which the fitment comes directly under the firebox. The main guide casting is an inverted U section, closed against ashes and the heat of the fire at the top. Fig. 114 is an illustration of a simpler arrangement. The horns are machined to an angle tangential to the desired radius, and the two axleboxes are tied together at the top by a crossbar with a lipped palm-piece at each end. The bearing springs are attached to a bridge resting on the crossbar.

In all radial axleboxes in which the axlebox moves up and down on the springs, as well as slides, the fitting of the

[115]

boxes in the guides must be very slack, otherwise the axle-box will jam when the axle is tilted. The radius chosen for the truck from the pivot to the axle, or for the horn-plates, as the case may be, should be rather larger than that nominally required.

To estimate the amount of clearance required between frames and bogie wheels (including pony trucks) a template of the proposed minimum curve should be laid alongside the elevation drawing of the engine. The centre of the curve should be placed against the centre of the rigid portion of the wheel base, as indicated in Fig. 115.

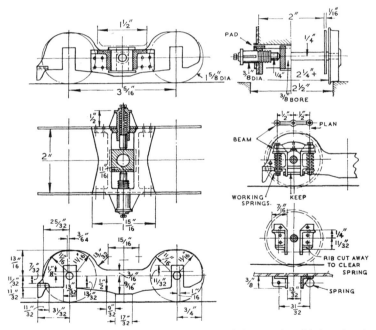

Fig. 119a.—Details of bogie frame, and horns for 2½-in. gauge S.R. "Pacific" locomotive.

CHAPTER VIII

CYLINDERS

Types of Cylinders

CYLINDERS in model-locomotive practice may be classified into five main groups:

(a) Inside cylinders with valves between, embodying many of the features of real practice up to the early part of this century.

(b) Inside cylinders with valves either on top or below the piston.

(c) Outside cylinders with steam chests between the frames.

(d) Outside cylinders with valves overhead.

(e) Multi-cylinders.

The standard British practice up to the advent of the super-heater is shown in the diagram Fig. 121 and photograph Fig. 122.

As will be seen, from the point of view of construction, subsequent repair, and packing of the spindles, this scheme has little to recommend itself to the model engineer. Furthermore, the cylinders are restricted in bore by the distance between the frames and the large amount of space taken up by the steam chest. A method that may be adopted to overcome maintenance difficulties to some extent is by mounting the cylinders, slide bars, motion plate and spindles on auxiliary frames, fitting between the main frames. The whole unit can then be withdrawn by removing a few bolts.

Two arrangements of inside cylinders are shown by the diagrams, Figs. 119 and 120. In the former scheme the valves are arranged at the sides,

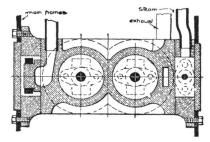

Fig. 119.—Cross-section of inside cylinders with valves located close to the frames.

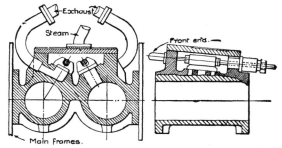

Fig. 120.—Inside cylinders with slide valves
inclined (in two planes).

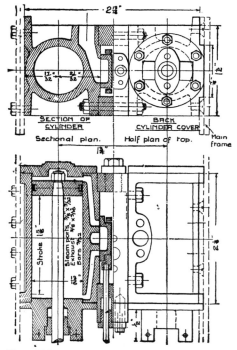

Fig. 121.—Arrangement of inside cylinders for ¾-in. scale model with valves
between.

close to the frames. The ports can be viewed through holes in the adjacent frames as the steam chest covers are readily removable. The second arrangement is adapted from one of the early L.N.W.R. engines of Ramsbottom's design.

Cylinders with Valves Below the Piston

Cylinders with valves below the pistons were used on British locomotives contemporary with those with valves between, and were considered superior in that the valves did not rest on the port faces when the engine was running with steam shut off. In addition, better draining of the cylinders was claimed for the design. Both these considerations have no great weight in model practice. The chief advantage for small models is that the valve can easily be inspected and set by turning the engine upside down and removing the steam chest cover. Further, the cylinders and valve chest are less cramped. A photograph of the arrangement is given by Fig. 123.

TABLE X

NOMINAL SIZES OF CYLINDERS

Gauge	Bore	Stroke
in.	in.	in.
$1\frac{3}{4}$	$\frac{7}{16}$ — $\frac{1}{2}$	$\frac{3}{4}$ — $\frac{13}{16}$
$2\frac{1}{2}$	$\frac{3}{4}$ — $\frac{7}{8}$	1 — $1\frac{1}{4}$
$3\frac{1}{2}$	1 — $1\frac{1}{4}$	$1\frac{5}{8}$ — $1\frac{3}{4}$
5	$1\frac{3}{8}$ — $1\frac{5}{8}$	$2\frac{1}{8}$ — $2\frac{3}{8}$
$7\frac{1}{4}$	$2\frac{1}{4}$ — 3	$3\frac{1}{4}$ — $3\frac{1}{2}$
$10\frac{1}{4}$	3 — 4	4 — $4\frac{3}{4}$
15	$4\frac{1}{4}$ — $5\frac{1}{4}$	$6\frac{1}{2}$ — $8\frac{1}{2}$

The author's design, evolved in 1902, is shown in Fig. 124. The steam passages are very simply arranged by drilling, the opening for the horizontal passage being stopped by a screw plug. As valves rusting or otherwise sticking on the spindle off the port faces is a source of trouble rather than an advantage in model practice the use of a spring to obviate the effects of gravity is essential and is included in the design. The valve chest may be placed parallel to the axes of the cylinders, as indicated on the drawing, or if the ordinary arrangement of

Fig. 122.—Inside cylinders assembled between auxilliary frames.

Fig. 123.—Two views of model locomotive chassis with valves below the cylinders and Stephenson's link motion.

(*Made by H. P. Jackson, Esq.*)

Stephenson's link motion (see Chapter X) is employed, then the surfaces must be inclined to suit the motion. As fitted by the author the valves were operated by a slip-eccentric valve gear, with sheaves outside the crank webs, through a rocking shaft.

Inside Cylinders: Valves on Top

The application of radial valve gears to model locomotives led to the adoption of cylinders with the valves on top. The

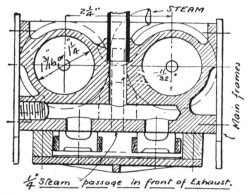

Fig. 124.—Cross section of inside cylinders with valves below.

arrangement of the passages has been modified by the author as shown in Fig. 125. The exhaust, which had been the difficulty with such cylinders, is led through the steam chest as indicated. This pipe has a taper thread at the bottom, so that by coating the screw with a little red lead and oil a good steam-tight joint is easily obtained, and the top joint is similarly made sound by a stuffing-box. By unscrewing the latter the steam chest cover can readily be removed for the inspection of the slide valves.

Considerable freedom in the matter of dimensions is obtained by adopting this design. In addition, the steam connections are of the simplest character. The exhaust leaves the cylinders in the centre, and is therefore in normal designs directly under the chimney.

The centres of the cylinders should not be placed at more than a scale equivalent of 2 ft. between, except in 2½-in. gauge engines where the usual standard is $1\frac{3}{4}$ S, where S is the scale of the model. The valve spindles may be in any convenient position so long as the valve can clear the exhaust pipe. Generally, to suit Joy's or other radial valve gear, which moves in the same plane as that of the connecting rod, the spindles are placed directly above the piston rods.

Fig. 126 is a cross section of a "valves-on-top" set of inside cylinders designed for a model 1-in. scale locomotive fitted with indirect Stephenson's link motion or Walschaerts' valve gear. In both these reversing gears the valve spindle is much more conveniently connected up if it is placed on one side or the other of the vertical line of the cylinders.

It is advisable to arrange inside cylinders (Fig. 127) of this

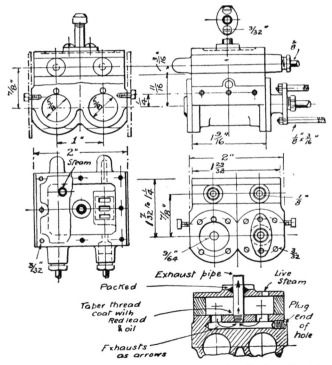

Fig. 125.—Details of 2½-in. gauge model cylinders (inside) with the slide valves arranged on top.

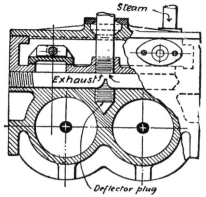

Fig. 126.—Inside cylinders with valves offset to suit inside Walschaerts' valve gear.

Fig. 127.—Arrangement of inside cylinders with valves on top.

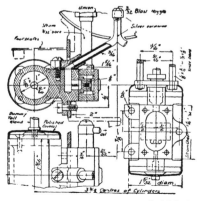

128.—Outside cylinders with slide valves between frames.

[123]

design with the lower fixing-flanges as high up as possible, so that the maximum clearance is obtained at points adjacent to bogie wheels and frames. In the 2½-in. gauge standard cylinders fixings to the frames are above the centre of the cylinders for this reason. In many modern engines the cylinders are not placed directly over the centre of the bogie, which renders some such precautions necessary.

Outside Cylinders: Valves Inside

With the valve chest inside the frames, outside cylinders are, in the larger model engines, entirely separate components on each side. Fig. 128 illustrates one of the author's designs. The exhaust pipes are made up in the form of an inverted Y—often termed "breeches pipes" because of their shape—and to get at the joint with the cylinder the opening in the main frames for the steam chest is scalloped out on the top. The design is arranged for 2½-in. gauge locomotives. In larger engines the ports are usually cast in, and the general scheme is similar to the cylinders applied to the 9½-in. gauge type shown in Fig. 129. In casting-in ports it is advisable to increase the thickness of the port bars slightly above the normal to ensure sound castings. For engines of medium size, say 1-in. scale, the exhaust ports only need be cast in. The steam ports are then end-milled down, and passages consisting of two or more holes, according to the size of the model, are drilled to meet these milled recesses. In coring the cylinder bore plenty of metal should always be provided in the walls to be machined. In the case of cylinders for 2½-in. gauge locomotives and smaller the castings are best cast quite solid and then roughly drilled to slightly less than the size of the bore. From this hole the cylinders can be machined where necessary, the bore being finished and lapped as a last operation. Emery should never be used for lapping gunmetal cylinders.

In view of the difficulties in aligning, supporting and arranging the pipes to and from separate outside cylinders the author designed a system, more particularly intended for locomotives of small gauge, in which a cross-connected steam chest is employed. The exhaust passages (see Fig. 132) are arranged within the walls of the steam chest. The advantage so obtained is that the chest itself forms a very stiff cross-stretcher for the main frame. Valve setting can be accomplished either

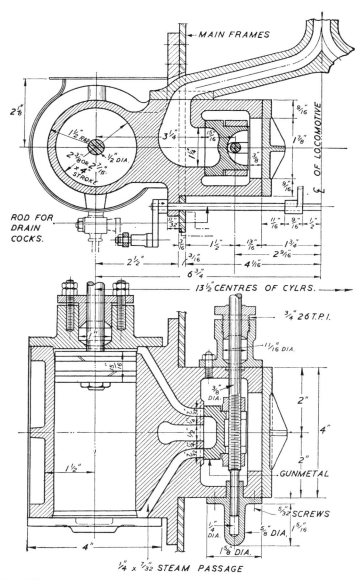

MAIN FRAMES

OF LOCOMOTIVE

ROD FOR
DRAIN
COCKS.

GUNMETAL

Fig. 129.—Outside cylinder with inside valve chest for 9½-in.
gauge, 2-in. scale "Atlantic" type locomotive.

[125]

by sight or by means of a plug jig with the ports cut in it (see Fig. 133). The whole of the work to the frames and cylinders may be done in the lathe and drilling machine.

The "all-circular" feature of the scheme is obtained by making the opening in the main frames out of centre. The spigot which fits this opening provides a surface for the joint of the exhaust passage. The horizontal passage for the exhaust

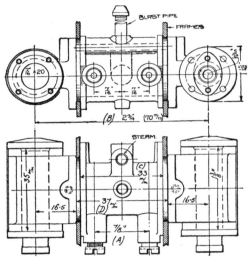

Fig. 130.—No. 1 gauge model outside cylinders with cross-connected steam chests.

is drilled right through the top of the steam chest casting as shown in the sections, Figs. 131 and 132. The latter drawing also indicates an arrangement of two plates, with notched edges to allow the steam to pass and with a spring between them, to ensure the valves always remaining on the port faces.

For a model of a "West Country" class locomotive the outside cylinders were fitted with cross-connected valve chests, the dummy valve heads being used as oil containers. (Fig. 135.)

Outside Cylinders: Valves on Top

Modern engines have outside cylinders with valves on the top and this development has been encouraged by the adoption

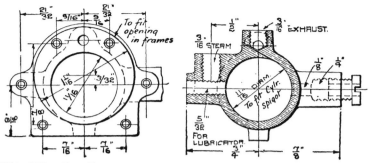

Fig. 131.—Details of the No. 1 gauge cylinders shown in Fig. 130.

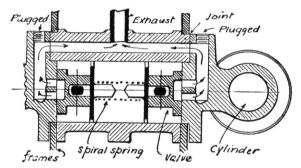

Fig. 132.—Cross-section of valve chest (Fig. 130).
Steam ports: 3/64-in. × 3/16-in.
Exhaust ,,   3/32-in. × 3/16-in.

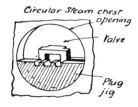

Fig. 133.—Method of setting
the slide valve with a plug-
jig. (See Fig. 132.)

[127]

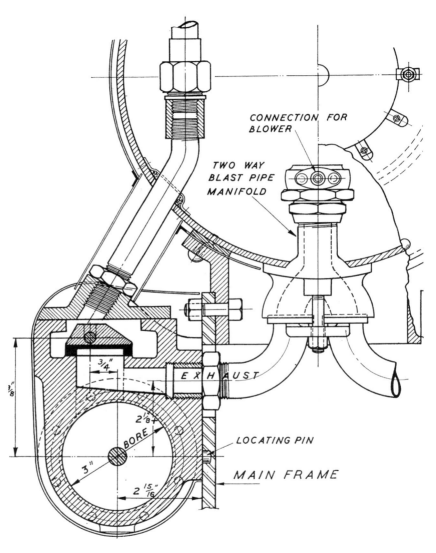

CONNECTION FOR BLOWER

TWO WAY BLAST PIPE MANIFOLD

EXHAUST

3/4"

3/8"

2 1/8"

BORE

3"

2 15/16"

LOCATING PIN

MAIN FRAME

g. 134.—Assembly of slide valve cylinder for the American 4-8-4 type locomotive in 7¼-in. gauge. (See also Fig. 6.)

[128]

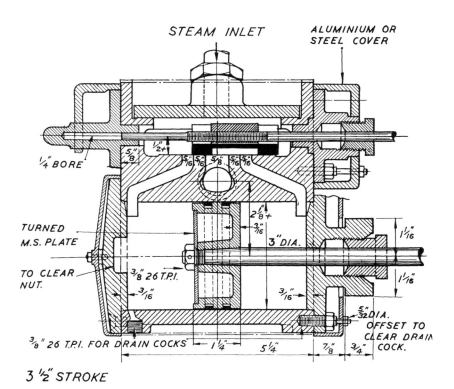

STEAM INLET

ALUMINIUM OR
STEEL COVER

$\frac{1}{4}''$ BORE

$\frac{5}{8}''$

$\frac{1}{2}''+$

$\frac{5}{16}''$ $\frac{5}{16}''$ $\frac{5}{8}''$ $\frac{5}{16}''$ $\frac{5}{16}''$

TURNED
M.S. PLATE

$2\frac{1}{8}''+$

$\frac{3}{16}''$

$3''$ DIA.

$1\frac{1}{16}''$

TO CLEAR
NUT.

$\frac{3}{8}''$ 26 T.P.I.

$\frac{3}{16}''$

$\frac{3}{16}''$

$1\frac{1}{16}''$

$\frac{5}{32}''$ DIA.
OFFSET TO
CLEAR DRAIN
COCK.

$\frac{3}{8}''$ 26 T.P.I. FOR DRAIN COCKS

$1\frac{1}{4}''$

$5\frac{1}{4}''$

$\frac{7}{8}''$

$\frac{3}{4}''$

$3\frac{1}{2}''$ STROKE

Fig. 134a.—Details of cylinders (Fig. 134).

of outside valve gears. The earlier examples had plain slide valves which were operated by link motion inside the frames, a rocking shaft transmitting the motion to the outside. The author adopted this scheme for 15-in. gauge engines he designed, the advantage claimed being ready access to the valves, port faces and glands. The superheater locomotive is fitted with piston valves, but these are not always adopted by amateurs.

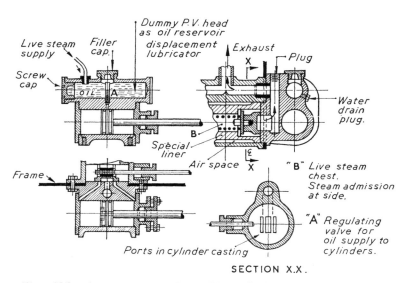

SECTION X.X.

Fig. 135.—Arrangement of outside cylinders for 2½-in. gauge model of West Country Class locomotive (S.R.).

Designs are shown in Figs. 134, 134a and 136 in which the external appearance of the piston-valve prototype is retained in conjunction with ordinary slide valves. The steam chest and cylinder body are separate castings screwed together, their end flanges being of such a profile that when connected up and covered by a sheet-steel lagging plate the illusion is complete.

With both Walschaerts' and the author's corrected valve gear the valve spindle is offset outwards in line with the gear. This tends to cramp the steam chest, but by placing the fixing

Fig. 136.—Assembly and parts of outside slide valve cylinders including cylinder block, steam chest, piston and valve.

Fig. 137.—Outside cylinder fitted with piston valves (note the two flanged covers on top of the cylinder for fitting the automatic water-release valves).

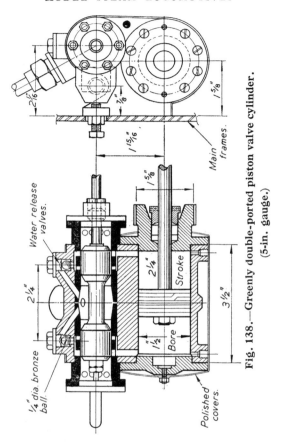

Fig. 138.—Greenly double-ported piston valve cylinder. (5-in. gauge.)

screws judiciously in the four corners of the steam chest a satis-factory fastening can be obtained.

The use of the ordinary gasfitters' running joints is a feature in the attachment of steam piping. The live steam pipe is secured by a running nipple and back nut. The nipple is threaded both inside and outside to the same pitch.

Multi-Cylinders

There are numerous examples of three- and four-cylinder locomotives employed on British Railways. The third and

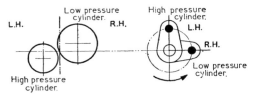

A. WORSDELL Two-Cylinder Scheme

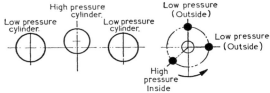

B. SMITH Three-Cylinder Scheme

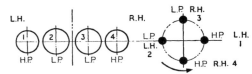

C. WEBB Four-Cylinder Scheme

Fig. 139.—Diagrams showing the setting-out of cylinders and cranks for Worsdell's, Smith's and Webb's compound systems.

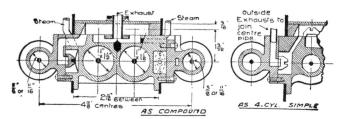

Fig. 140.—3¼-in gauge (11/16-in. scale) four-cylinder arrangement for either compound or simple. For the compound system, exhaust steam from the high-pressure outside cylinder is exhausted to the receiver and steam chest above the inside low-pressure cylinder. It is admitted to the inside cylinder by a slide valve on top (not shown) and is again exhausted in the usual way to the central blast pipe as shown.

[133]

fourth cylinders are located between the frames and below the smoke-box—usually well forward when it is required to take the drive off the front coupled axle. Models of these multi-cylinder prototypes are often designed with these inside cylinders omitted. Such two-cylinder engines in the large gauge are generally powerful enough for all passenger hauling purposes.

When the models are designed with a complete set of cylinders, provision has to be made for the appropriate valve gear between the frames. In some instances it is not always possible to include the extra mechanism in the narrow space available. The difficulty can be obviated to some extent by adopting a conjugated valve gear scheme, particularly for three-cylinder models. Alternatively a simple slip-eccentric valve motion can be employed for the inside cylinder which is independent of the outside gears yet at the same time will reverse automatically.

In the case of the G.W.R. locomotives, there are certain limitations, since, in order to follow the design of the prototype faithfully, the valve gear must be located between the frames and linked by means of a rocking arm to the outside valve rod. The two-cylinder arrangement, however, presents no serious difficulty in this respect.

Compound Systems

The Smith three-cylinder compound system of the Midland Railway with its single high-pressure cylinder between the frames and two low-pressure cylinders outside can be adopted for models from $3\frac{1}{2}$ in. gauge and upwards. The low-pressure cylinder cranks are set at 90° (Fig. 139). The exhaust steam from the high-pressure cylinder passes into a "receiver" before being admitted to the respective outside cylinders. In order to ensure dry steam being admitted to the low-pressure cylinders, the receiver can be made in the form of a superheater or dryer located in the smokebox. The outside valves can be actuated by Walschaerts' or other radial gear and for simplicity the inside valve could be controlled by the simple slip-eccentric gear. Arrangements can also be made for live steam to be admitted to the receiver direct for the engine to work as a non-compound when starting. For a model all three cylinders can be the same diameter, otherwise the low-pressure cylinder is larger than the high pressure cylinder in the proportion of approximately 1·1 to 1.

[134]

In the Webb four-cylinder compound two low-pressure cylinders are placed between the frames. Exhaust steam from the high-pressure cylinder is passed through a short receiver to the adjacent inside cylinder. The ratio of the respective high- and low-pressure cylinders is of the order of 1·35 to 1.

The Worsdell system consists of one inside high-pressure cylinder and an inside low-pressure cylinder. The low-pressure cylinder is inclined above the normal centre-line of the axles and the second cylinder is inclined below the centre-line in order that they may be accommodated between the frames.

A four-cylinder compound arrangement is illustrated in Fig. 140. Where four cylinders of the same size are employed it would be quite simple to rearrange the passages to use high-pressure steam in all of them. In either case the inside and outside cranks would be placed at 180° to each other, and one set of valve gear employed on each side. Some form of rocking-shaft gear would then be necessary to transmit the motion in a diametrically opposite direction from one spindle to the other.

Pistons

In all model locomotive work, owing to the low piston speed, pistons should be accurate in diameter, a close running fit in the cylinder, and should be comparatively long. The writer uses for the approximate minimum thickness the rule $0·3S + \frac{1}{16}$, where S is the stroke of the piston in inches. Further, the piston should never have less than $\frac{1}{10}$ in. plain portion at each end, and of necessity should be truly concentric and in alignment with the piston rod. The piston is the heart of the model, and most models fail to give the best results because of pistons which are faulty either in design or workmanship, or in both. Many a boiler or system of firing has been condemned when the real trouble has been waste of steam in the cylinders.

Where the lathe available is insufficiently accurate, the small model is best fitted with a piston packed with hemp or asbestos yarn (Fig. 141). Piston rings have been successfully made for cylinders as small as $\frac{1}{2}$-in. bore. The design for a $\frac{1}{2}$-in. scale engine shows a piston for a $\frac{11}{16}$-in. gunmetal cylinder the ring is of steel and should be machined about ·002 in. larger than the bore. The slot should be filed at an angle with a fine three-cornered file from the inside, so that the width of the slot is such that it almost closes when the piston is inserted in the cylinder. Great care must be taken not to distort the ring. The ring should fit the slot freely, but without shake longitudinally. If there is any suspicion of an opening in the slot asbestos yarn may be tucked into it before assembling the piston. Designs for 3½ in. and 5 in. gauge pistons are included.

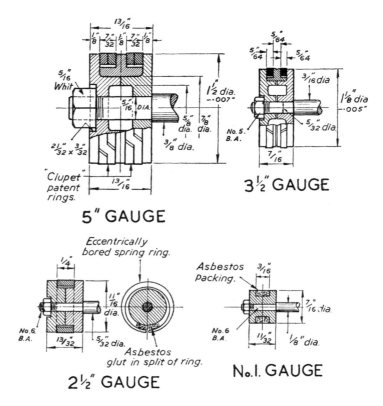

Fig. 141.—Types of model pistons in four gauges.

[136]

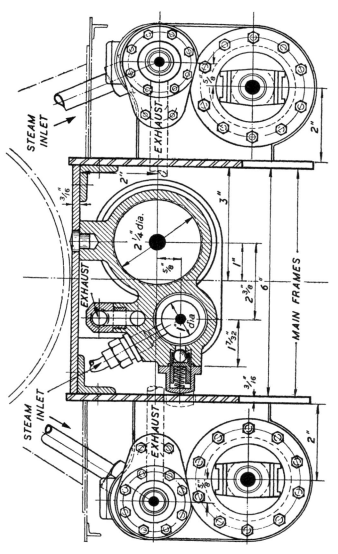

Fig. 145.—Three-cylinder system for 7¼-in gauge "Pacific".

Steam Cut-off

"Cut-off" is the term used to denote the position of the piston in its path at the moment the valve is closing the port to admission of steam to the cylinder. From this point onwards the steam remaining in the cylinder does its work expansively. Cut-off is usually expressed as a percentage value of the whole piston stroke and its maximum value in model work (as in real practice) seldom exceeds 85 per cent.

The various methods of operating the valves and for reversing are described in the next chapter.

Materials

In no case should soft yellow brass be used as cylinder material. If non-ferrous metals are employed a hard gunmetal is essential. Bronze pistons and valves are also advisable. Nickel silver (nickel and copper) is a material only recommended for piston rods and valve spindles of small models because it is less likely to rust when the engine is not in service, although with care—i.e. first draining and then oiling the cylinders thoroughly —steel rods give no trouble. Steel valves and steel piston rings wear very well in conjunction with well lubricated gunmetal or cast-iron cylinders. Gunmetal cylinders require liberal lubrication when supplied with dry steam. In all cases super-heated steam should be used only in conjunction with a mechanical or other efficient system of lubrication. Gunmetal or bronze slide valves work very well on cast-iron cylinders. For cylinders of large models cast-iron pistons and rings working in hard cast-iron cylinders are widely employed.

Piston Valve Cylinders

With the introduction of the superheater locomotive and increased boiler pressures in real locomotive practice, the ordinary slide valve has been largely superseded by the piston type valve. For the larger gauges—$3\frac{1}{2}$ in. gauge and upwards piston valve cylinders can be employed. It is sometimes the practice, however to retain the slide valve and to disguise the exterior to represent the piston valve cylinder.

The piston valve functions in the same way as the slide valve—the proportions for lap and lead are calculated as in the case of slide valves. Fig. 137 shows a typical example of

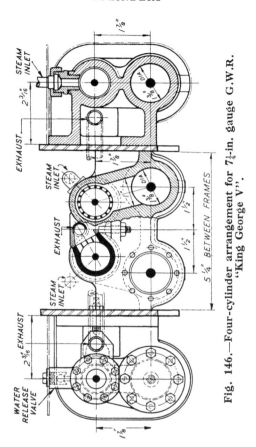

Fig. 146.—Four-cylinder arrangement for 7¼-in. gauge G.W.R. "King George V".

ordinary piston valve cylinder. The valve is of the inside admission type, viz.: live steam is admitted between the twin valve heads. It will be observed that the valve spindle and gland box are subject only to the lower exhaust steam pressure. The exhaust steam is collected at both ends of the valve chamber and led through suitable passages to the exhaust pipe and manifold.

Probably a serious defect that may be encountered with the standard pattern valve head is cross leakage of steam to the exhaust chamber. There is usually not enough room to

[141]

fit an adequate number of piston rings. By adopting the author's double-ported piston valve arrangement cross leakage is considerably reduced. The arrangement shown in Fig. 138 exemplifies the scheme.

Water release valves are fitted above each valve head in order to prevent damage to cylinder heads etc., by trapped condense in the system.

Exhaust Pressures

Exhaust steam from locomotive cylinders has to provide the essential blast in the smokebox to induce the hot flue gases through the boiler tubes from the firebox. In full size locomotive practice, the exhaust pressures are from 2% to 4% of boiler pressure. For a model an exhaust pressure of 10 lb. per square inch (gauge) will induce a sharp blast for carrying away the waste products of combustion in the tubes. Therefore, the expansion of steam in a model which has a boiler pressure not exceeding 50 lb. per square inch cannot be continued. The valve lap therefore must not be very large in proportion to its total travel. By arranging a small proportion of lap and by advancing the valve, "lost motion" in the valve gear mechanism is to some extent obviated. Heat losses are unavoidably high

Fig. 147.—Details of a set of piston-valve cylinder castings with cast-in ports.

and increase when steam is expanded excessively by too early a cut-off. These losses can be reduced by a certain degree of superheating.

Piston valve heads are fitted with split and solid rings alternately. The valve should be allowed to "float" freely on its spindle without having longitudinal displacement. Shims can be fitted for making the necessary adjustments for lap. The bore of the liner should be lapped to a fine finish and at the entry slightly coned. The rings, both solid and split, must be ground on their respective valve heads to the correct diameter. The gaps should close; the free gap not exceeding ·005 in. The slot in the ring is machined away from the inside. Cast-iron or steel rings should be specified, particularly in the case of a super-heated steam supply.

The dimensions given in Table X, page 119, for the cylinder bores are nominally for two-cylinder engines. For three-cylinder (simple) designs these dimensions can be reduced by 18% and for four-cylinder (simple) locomotives by an amount approximating to nearly 30%. For correct design, consideration must also be given to the tractive effort of the engine as stated in Chapter III, page 40, in order to correlate the size of cylinders.

CHAPTER IX

VALVE GEARING: SIMPLE REVERSING MOTIONS

A LOCOMOTIVE without some means of reversing would be unacceptable even to a beginner in model engineering and while many of the valve gears are complicated and their action intricate, a locomotive can be made to reverse with comparatively simple mechanisms.

Before describing the principles and methods of construction of the various types of valve gears the fundamental difference between a valve *without* lap and a valve *with* lap must be defined.

Simple Slide Valve

The setting of a slide valve without lap ("simple valve") is timed exactly 90° in advance or retard of the crank pin. When the crank is on its dead centre and the piston at the beginning of its stroke, the valve is in its central position, all ports are covered, and on the point of opening at one end to admit steam to the cylinder. Steam can, however, pass to the exhaust port due to the edge-to-edge contact of the valve faces (Fig. 148). Steam is also admitted to the cylinder for the whole length of the stroke of the piston which is wasteful and affords no control of the sequence of operations. The indicator diagram (viz.: pressure in the cylinder at any point in the stroke of the piston) is not ideal as shown by Fig. 149A. Oscillating cylinders with the same timing (90° advance) give the same indicator curve. For small toy models the arrangement is sufficiently satisfactory owing to the low .piston speed and to the fact that, due to excessive condensation present in very small cylinders, no great saving is observed in introducing an expansion for the steam.

Valve With Lap

The skilled model engineer and experimenter will, however, desire a greater degree of perfection than such a simple slide valve will provide. The introduction of quite a small amount of lap—over and above that necessary to prevent cross leakage—

Cross leakage

SIMPLE VALVE
NO LAP.

VALVE WITH
SMALL LAP.

NORMAL VALVE

Fig. 148.—Simple slide valve without lap permits direct cross-leakage to the exhaust port. A small amount of lap prevents this leakage,

into the proportions of the slide valve improves the theoretical indicator diagram immensely. In actual working a much sweeter motion will be produced at the higher speeds.

It is essential that the valve should be on the point of opening at the beginning of the piston stroke. Therefore, when a valve with an appreciable amount of lap is employed, the eccentric must be advanced as shown in Fig. 150. The advantage of this

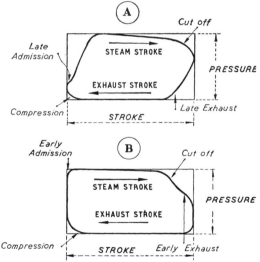

Fig. 149.—(a) Theoretical indicator diagram for simple slide valve without lap. Late admission of steam at beginning of stroke, drop in pressure and late exhaust. (b) Indicator diagram for slide valve with lap. Early admission of steam at beginning of stroke, full pressure up to the point of cut-off and an early exhaust.

K

[145]

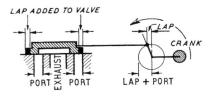

Fig. 150.—The addition of lap to a valve. The eccentric is advanced by an amount equal to the lap.

is shown in the indicator diagram, Fig. 149B. A definite amount of lead can be provided as necessary. As the relative position of the valve must be observed for the opposite direction of rotation, the eccentric in this reverse position *must not be diametrically opposite* its forward position, as will be seen by reference to Fig. 152. This is fundamental and excludes many simple reversing devices.

Designs of Valve Gears

The only extremely simple reversing gear which allows a valve with lap to function properly is that commonly known

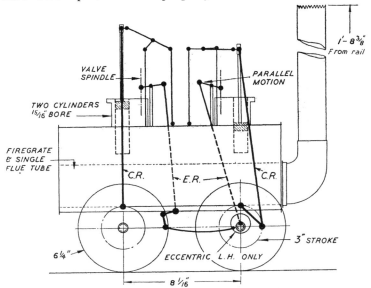

Fig. 151.—Diagram of valve gear for 7¼-in. gauge working model of Stephenson's "Locomotion No. 1"—1825.

as the slip-eccentric gear. In the more popular "link motions" it is usual to provide two eccentrics, one for operating the valve in the forward direction and the other for the backward direction of the locomotive. A slotted link is used to engage either one or the other of the eccentrics with the valve spindle. The Stephenson's gear is chief among these motions.

The radial valve gears, such as Walschaerts' and Joy's require the addition of a second motion, which, synchronizing with either the slotted link or angular slide reversing device, as the case may be, produces at the valve spindle a timing of the valve which is almost identical with that produced from an eccentric which is advanced beyond the normal 90°. The angle of advance of an eccentric is the angle it is moved in advance of the normal 90° and not the total angle it is advanced in front of the crank pin.

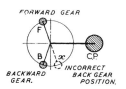

Fig. 152.—Diagram showing the relative positions of forward and backward eccentrics when the valve is provided with lap. The reverse eccentric (b) as shown dotted at "x" is incorrect, relative to the crank pin CP.

The second motion is usually taken from the horizontal movement of the crosshead or the connecting rod. It is apparent, therefore, that when the valve gear is in its mid-gear position, the only motion the valve spindle obtains is that from the movement of the crosshead or connecting rod. When the crosshead is at one end of its stroke the valve is then on the point of opening to steam admission at that end. At the other extremity of the stroke, the same thing happens in the reverse direction. This function exemplifies the difference between the incidence of the valve movements of a slide valve with lap and one which is without lap. The simple or lapless valve does not move with the reversing lever in mid-gear.

The normal valve, i.e. the valve with lap, moves to the extent of the lap when the driver's lever in the cab is in a central position.

Simple Reversing Valve

The advantage of the 90° timing arrangement with the

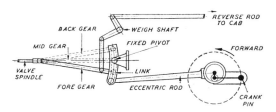

Fig. 153.—Obsolete type of link motion for reversing

simple no-lap valve is that reversing can be effected from the cab of the model engine by changing over a steam-to-exhaust cock and vice-versa. A piston or a spring-loaded slide valve is essential in such a case. By turning the cock through 90° the steam passage to the cylinder becomes the exhaust and the exhaust passage becomes the inlet for steam.

The other alternative for a "no-lap" slide valve is to introduce some form of link or slide arrangement which will diametrically reverse the valve movement and thereby change the direction of rotation of the shaft. This can be done in two ways: the motion of the eccentric can be reversed by means of a curved link mechanism or by a pivoted slide arrangement.

Single Eccentric Curved Link Gear

This is an obsolete form of link reversing gear and the eccentric is set 90° in advance of the crank pin CP. (Fig. 153). A simple valve with only sufficient lap to prevent cross leakage is required. When the position of the valve spindle is known, the setting out of the gear can proceed. The length of the working portion of the slotted link (or expansion link) should not be less than 3·5 to 4 times the *valve* travel. Where the valve

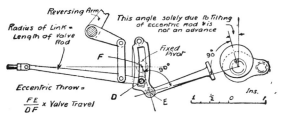

Fig. 154.—Method of setting-out a single-eccentric link motion.

[148]

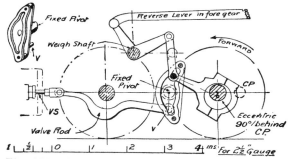

Fig. 155.—"Gab" type single eccentric link reversing gear.

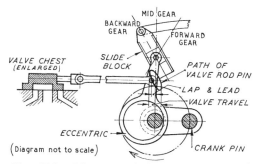

Fig. 156.—Diagram of Hackworth's radial
valve gear.

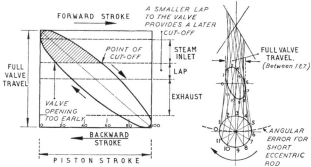

Fig. 157.—Diagrams showing the motion of
Hackworth's gear and valve events.

[149]

spindle is on the same centre line as the driving motion (Fig. 154) then the eccentric will not be placed 90° in advance of the crank pin as in the case of the first example. In the former case the valve spindle is above that of the motion. Wherever it is located, however, the relative movement as transmitted to the link must be the same. The design of the link will also have some influence. With a link as shown, the eccentric travel is greater than the valve travel, as owing to the arrangement of the pivots, the link acts as a reducing lever for the motion. With a box link, where the connections of the eccentric rod coincide, the throw of the sheave will be equal to the valve travel, plus a small amount to make up for lost motion and wear.

There is no exact rule as to the respective lengths of valve lever (or radius rod) and eccentric-rod, but it is better if they are equal.

When the valve rod is lifted by means of the reversing arm from the forward gear position to that of mid-gear, the reciprocating motion of the valve rod ceases. In the back-gear position, above the horizontal centre line, the motion of the valve spindle is completely reversed relative to the eccentric rod and the direction of rotation of the crank-pin is changed.

The single eccentric curved-link gear is totally unsuitable for operating a valve with the normal amount of lap. The valve would, as a consequence, be timed just as much late on reverse as it would be advanced on the forward stroke. There is no means of correcting it other than by the introduction of a second eccentric.

Single Eccentric (Open) Link Gear

This is an unusual form of single eccentric motion in which it is impossible to arrange for any intermediate valve movement (Fig. 155). The gear is not perfect for each port opening, but its function is worthy of consideration. Vertical movement of the crank axle should be reduced to a minimum. The slotted link is fixed to a plate pivoted to the main frame. The eccentric rod lies between the plate and the link and has a projecting die pin on the end which also engages the end of the lifting links, so that a reversal of the motion may be obtained by the levers. The gear can be said to be a relic of one of the very early "gab" motions.

[150]

Hackworth Gear

The original slide-block reversing motion was invented by J. W. Hackworth in 1858. In this gear an eccentric or short crank on the same centre line as the crank pin is employed (Fig. 156). The vertical movement of the trunnion block when the slide is tilted governs the main opening and reversing of the valve, and the horizontal motion governs the opening of the valve to advance. This advance is equal to twice the lap plus twice the lead. It will be observed from the diagram, Fig. 157, that the port openings cannot be equalized due to errors of angularity for the short eccentric rod.

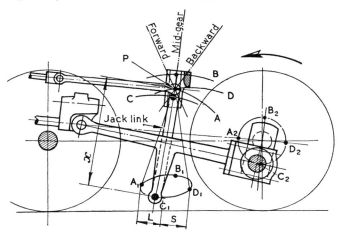

Fig. 158.—Point-path diagram of jack-link connecting rod and slide block of the Greenly (uncorrected) valve gear.

Greenly's (Slide Block) Gear

The motion derived from the up and down vibrations of a connecting rod or crank pin has exactly the same timing as an eccentric placed at 90° to the crank. This circumstance is a fundamental one, and is employed in the author's modification of Joy's gear. Errors are, however, introduced due to the angularity of rods or links connecting up the moving parts. These are much in excess of those experienced in an ordinary 90° eccentric gear, and upset either the timing (viz. point of steam admission and cut-off) or the magnitude of the port opening. This is apparent from the point-path diagram (Fig. 158).

[151]

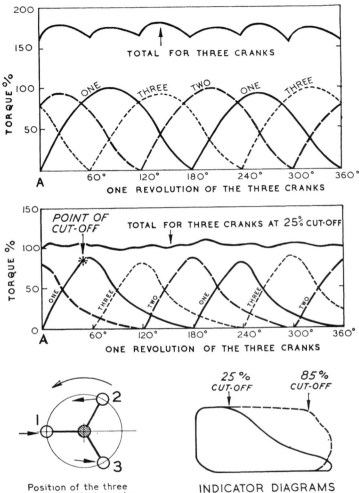

Fig. 159.—Crank-effort diagrams for a three-cylinder, 5-in. gauge model locomotive. (At 85% cut off the total turning effort for a complete cycle fluctuates most noticeably and has six distinct beats, whereas by linking up to 25% cut off the turning effort attains greater uniformity and provides better conditions for running.)

One or the other of these errors may be almost entirely eliminated in a valve with minimum lap by making the vertical vibrating lever as long as possible from the lug C_1 to the slide block P. (Fig. 158.) As will be seen from the arcs C and D the travel of the valve is unequal. This error can be reduced only by a long lug on the connecting rod, a short piston stroke and the greatest possible vertical distance between piston rod and valve spindle.

The fault is not important in a small engine. The dimensions L and S are together equal to the stroke and it is this component

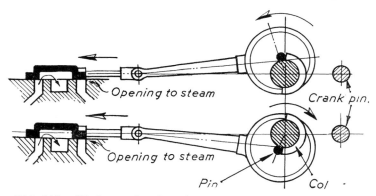

Fig. 160.—Diagram showing the setting of the slip-eccentric for reversing.

of the movement that is responsible for the error. The port bars—between the steam and exhaust ports—should be ample in thickness in order to provide for unequal valve travel and to prevent cross leakage of steam to the exhaust cavity.

In the example illustrated in Fig. 158 a normal amount of lap is given to the valve. With a comparatively long vibrating lever, there is no difficulty in making this small. The steam distribution is fairly good in full gear, but bad when any attempt is made to "link up" for earlier cut-offs.

Slip Eccentric Valve Gear

The slip—or loose eccentric valve gear—is a simple and efficient model locomotive reversing motion. It was used on the "Rocket" for reversing in conjunction with a hand gear for

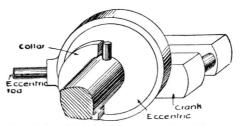

Fig. 161.—Simple slip-eccentric with stop
pin fixed in axle.

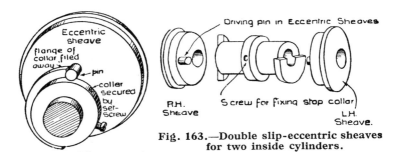

Fig. 162.—Slip eccentric
with stop collar fitted
to axle.

Fig. 163.—Double slip-eccentric sheaves
for two inside cylinders.

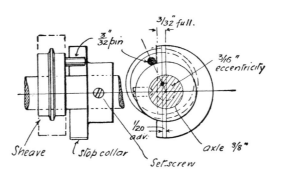

Fig. 164.—Assembly of stop collar and slip-
eccentric sheave

starting. The gear was also employed on the famous Webb three-cylinder compound engines of the L.N.W.R. to control the valve of the single low-pressure cylinder.

The slip eccentric gear is not of much use in engines on which the driver rides because it cannot be controlled in a sufficiently simple manner from the cab. As shown in Fig. 152, with the slight advance that is desirable to make a model run sweetly, an eccentric should take up positions approximating to F and B. To accomplish this, the single eccentric is made loose on the shaft or axle and is operated by a stud, stop or other driving pin in either one position or the other. The effect is to make the engine continue to run in the direction it is started on.

If the relative position of the crank pin is moved something less than half a turn, then the locomotive will travel in the opposite direction. Fig. 160 illustrates the principle and Fig. 161 shows one method of driving the eccentric with a pin fixed in the axle. As the accuracy of the valve setting is dependent to a large extent on that of the drilling of the axle, the method shown in Fig. 162, which provides for the correction of any errors in workmanship, is recommended. In this example a stop pin is placed anywhere in the side face of the eccentric sheave, preferably exactly on the major axis. A flanged collar, with half its flange cut away, is fitted to the axle. This collar is fixed on to the axle, and if two collars are used adjustment of their positions may be made separately for each side.

For the outside-cylinder locomotive a double collar (Fig. 163) is employed with stop flanges machined at 90°. Here the eccentric must be accurately drilled as the only adjustment that can be applied is that of altering the amount of lap and lead to suit. The marking out and drilling is, however, less likely to be accompanied by inaccuracies than the method of fixing a pin in the axle. The setting-out diagram shows the method for proportioning the valve lap, eccentrics and stop collar.

CHAPTER X

VALVE GEARING: LINK AND RADIAL VALVE GEARS

LOCOMOTIVE valve gears are divided into two main classes: (1) Link motions and (2) Radial valve gears.

For the link motions, the amount of lead given to a valve varies with the amount of cut-off. The lead increases as the cut-off is made earlier and vice versa. What is sometimes termed "negative lead" may be advantageous for larger types of locomotives running on garden railways. But this will depend on the conditions of working generally. It is introduced to prevent excessive lead in the mid-gear position. In full gear, however, lead is entirely absent and does not begin to function until a certain degree of "linking up" or earlier cut-off is accomplished.

In the radial type gear, the lead is a constant quantity for all points of cut-off.

A selection of the various types of link and radial gears employed in locomotive practice, both past and present, is listed below:

LINK MOTIONS	RADIAL VALVE GEARS
Stephenson 1841	Walschaerts' 1844
Howe 1844	Hackworth 1859
Gooch	Marshall 1879
Allan	Joy
	Greenly
	Baker

Stephenson's Link Motion

Stephenson's link-reversing gear has two eccentrics, one for each direction of motion and each with the necessary advance (Fig. 165). The eccentric rods are connected at their ends by a curved and slotted link which, besides providing a convenient method of reversing the motion, maintains the angle of advance necessary where a valve with a lap is employed in all positions of the reversing lever. This important function gives the driver the opportunity of altering the point of cut-off and availing himself

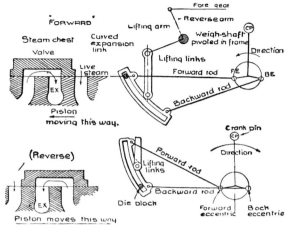

Fig. 165.—Forward and reverse positions for Stephenson's link motion.

of the expansive force of steam. This not only provides perfect control over the power developed in the cylinders, independently of the main steam supply (i.e. the position of the regulator), but results in economy in steam and fuel and much sweeter running of the engine at high speeds. While the variable cut-off is not of paramount importance in a small model, a valve with some lap and an advance of the eccentrics equal to that lap is very desirable. In larger engines it is an essential.

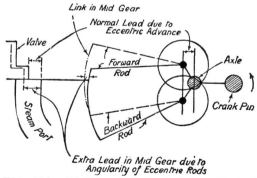

Fig. 166.—Diagram illustrating the effect of angularity of rods in Stephenson's link motion.

In the case of the Stephenson motion the lead increases as the lever is brought nearer to mid-gear, and this function in small models can be made use of to eliminate the necessity for advancing the eccentrics. Even in larger models the advance of the eccentric is made slightly less than the lap because of this characteristic, which, by the way, is peculiar to the Stephenson gear when open rods are used. With crossed rods the effect is negative. The angularity of the rods—which, of course, is greater with short rods—is responsible for this, and is illustrated by the diagram (Fig. 166). The test for the amount of this increased "lead" is to place the big end on dead centre and to operate the reversing lever. The valve spindle will move slightly in the direction of opening the port as the lever approaches mid-gear.

The effect is more noticeable with the form of link illustrated in Fig. 167 than with a "launch-engine" type of link usually employed where short rods and small-throw eccentrics are essential. Fig. 168 shows this type of link, which should, if possible, be avoided in small models owing to the difficulty of getting the eccentric-rod pins sufficiently close to the curved slot to prevent excessive slip on the die. Where the launch-type of link is used the slot should be much longer than apparently necessary to allow for this objectionable up-and-down movement of the die. The eccentric travel may also be made equal to the valve travel. With the loco-type of link there is a reducing effect due to the link acting as a lever, and the eccentric throw must be increased (with a given valve travel) in proportion. A model several times full size may be made to investigate this, as shown by Fig. 169, v equalling half the valve travel and E the eccentricity of the sheaves. In this model the link is set out quite straight and the diagram pinned on to a rotating block. The pivot on the end of a *long* valve rod representing the die should be movable along the slot between the limits Q, and attaching the valve rod to a model of the slide valve, the effect of reversing and linking up may be observed with reasonable accuracy. The required eccentricity of the sheave may also be settled arithmetically. With a link as shown by Fig. 170, the eccentricity of the sheave will equal $\frac{P}{Q}$ × half valve travel.

As a rule, if Q is divided into three parts P will measure

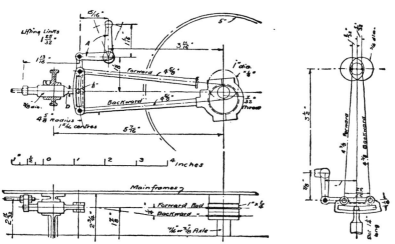

Fig. 167.—Stephenson's link motion for 3¼-in. gauge model.

Fig. 168.—Launch-type link motion.

five of these parts, therefore eccentricity of sheave must be 5/3 times the valve travel, or P = 1·67Q.

The working portion of the slot of Q (Fig. 170) should in all cases be not less than 3½ times the valve travel. The length overall will depend on the size of the pins and curved slot employed. The eccentric rods and straps should be made to dead length between centres. Especially where several engines

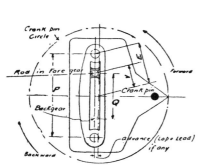

Fig. 169.—A method of setting-out for link motion.

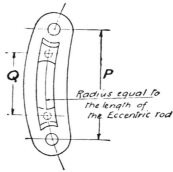

Fig. 170.—Curved Link as used in Locomotives.

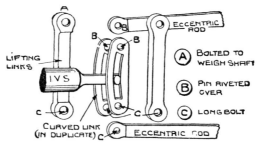

Fig. 171.—Details of components for link
motion.

are being built, they should be tested for length on a jig. The
sheaves being correctly set in relation to the crank pin, all that
is necessary to obtain a perfect timing is to adjust the position
of the valve on its spindle so that it opens at the same point in
the stroke in each direction and at each end of the cylinders.
Several forms of adjustment are available. The amount of the
port opening may vary slightly at full port, but so long as the
"timing" of the admission is correct this does not matter very
much.

Simple Link Motion

The illustration (Fig. 167) shows a straightforward arrangement of link motion as applied, say to a 4-4-0 type outside-
cylinder model. The gear is
said to have "open rods." The
crank pin would be at R.H.
dead centre. If the forward
eccentric were connected to
the bottom of the link the
arrangement would be termed
a "crossed-rod" gear, and
there would be less advance
in mid-gear—exactly the
opposite result to that
obtained in the "open rod"
motion.

The lifting arm of the
weigh shaft supports the

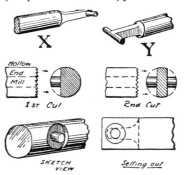

Fig. 172.—Method of making an
intermediate valve spindle and
die pin from solid bar, employing
a hollow-end-mill cutter.

[160]

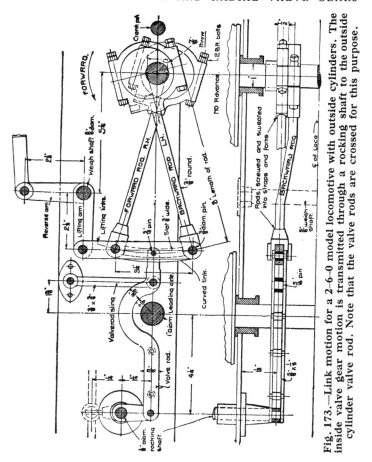

Fig. 173.—Link motion for a 2–6–0 model locomotive with outside cylinders. The inside valve gear motion is transmitted through a rocking shaft to the outside cylinder valve rod. Note that the valve rods are crossed for this purpose.

curved link and eccentric rods by means of the lifting links, and in large models, is counterbalanced. The lifting links are connected, for simplicity, to the bottom joint of the curved link. The die-block is solid with the intermediate spindle, a practice recommended by the author in small engines. This arrangement, coupled with the use of duplicate curved links (as sketched in Fig. 171), cuts out the forking of the eccentric rod ends. As in this case the valve spindle is close to the frames (a common happening), the guided intermediate spindle has a lug on its

L   [161]

forward end to receive the spindle and two adjusting and securing nuts. The backward eccentric rod, being the least used, is set over, the forward one being straight and in line with the rest of the motion. The angle (A) between the lifting arm and reversing arm of the weigh shaft will depend on the position of the reverse lever or wheel in the cab. The angle is usually less than 90°. As the proximity of the boiler may require the weigh shaft to be close to the horizontal centre line of motion, it may be necessary to cut away the underside of the shaft to clear the forward rod when in back gear.

The die on the intermediate valve spindle should be machined out of the solid. It is essential that the vertical dimension D (Fig. 167) in all link motions should be reduced to the minimum, otherwise a permanently "linked-up" state will obtain and much of the valve travel will be lost. This can be done with a hollow end mill, one side at a time, as indicated in Fig. 172, and the superfluous metal filed away. Pattern x is required for the valve gear (Fig. 167) and y for the link motion (Fig. 178). In the latter case curved links in duplicate and this form of intermediate spindle die-block are strongly recommended, so that the slot can be placed more closely than otherwise possible to the eccentric-rod joints.

Photo: H. Greenly

Fig. 174.—Walschaerts' valve gear for outside slide-valve cylinders of a large-scale model locomotive.

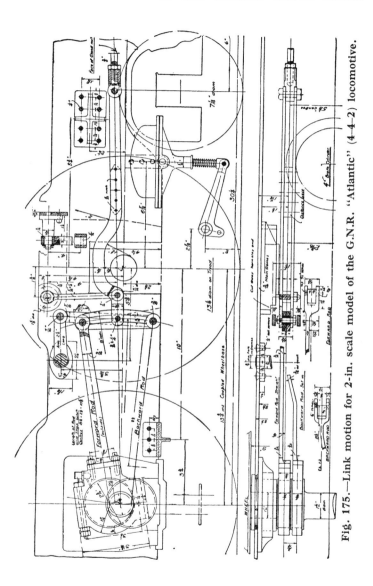

Fig. 175.—Link motion for 2-in. scale model of the G.N.R. "Atlantic" (4-4-2) locomotive.

Both motions are designed for $3\frac{1}{2}$-in. gauge, but would with modification, suit a smaller locomotive.

Alternative Stephenson's Link Motion

Another arrangement of Stephenson's motion is illustrated in Fig. 173. Here the valve gear actuates the slide valves through a rocking shaft. As these rocking shaft and levers reverse the movement of the die the eccentrics have to be placed exactly opposite to their usual position which involves crossing the rods. The negative effect on the advance is not, however, observed, as the rocking shaft changes it into a positive one. Although the model to which this gear is fitted is a large one ($7\frac{1}{4}$ in. gauge) no advance of eccentrics is provided, but the valve has a considerable lap. It has proved quite successful, and has burnt no more fuel nor consumed more water than a similar model in 5 in. gauge. This arrangement shows how difficulties arising from the close proximity of the coupled axles have been overcome.

Fig. 175 illustrates the Stephenson's link motion for a 2-in. scale model G.N.R. "Atlantic" locomotive. A slung valve rod, holding the die, takes the place of the usual sliding intermediate valve spindle. The boiler of this engine is large, and there is little clearance between the top of the forward rod and this shaft when the motion is in back gear. This rod must therefore be cast or forged to eliminate the need for any large boss at the root of the lifting arms.

Although now obsolete for express engines the front-coupled wheel arrangement is employed for tank engines. The valve gear (Fig. 176) is representative of this, and is designed to suit a 1-in. scale model of the L.B.S.C.R. historic "Gladstone" type. The valves are below the cylinders and the motion is inclined. In setting out the eccentrics, they must be dealt with as in a case where the crank-pin dead centre coincides with the line of the valve motion. Actually the crank and eccentrics are respectively displaced to the amount of the angle between the centre lines of the two motions.

A standard arrangement of this valve gear was designed for an ex-L.N.E.R. $7\frac{1}{4}$-in. gauge model locomotive. As in Fig. 177 the curved link is solid and is fitted with a hardened die, the eccentric rods being forked in the orthodox manner. As the rods are long and the angular effects small the eccentrics

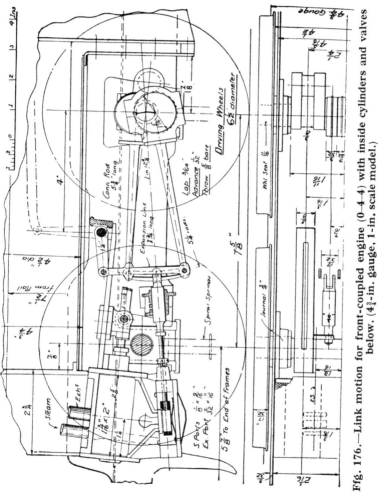

Fig. 176.—Link motion for front-coupled engine (0-4-4) with inside cylinders and valves below. ($4\frac{3}{4}$-in. gauge, 1-in. scale model.)

are advanced more than usual. The position of the valve is adjusted by turning the valve spindle, one end of which is screwed into the intermediate spindle, the other being of a bobbin shape and revolving in the slot in the back of the valve.

Fig. 177 shows an arrangement of link motion for an engine with outside cylinders in which the eccentric rods are long and embrace the leading coupled axle. The boiler and driving wheels are both of large diameter and the weigh shaft cannot be placed in a position that will allow the reversing arm to clear the wheels and boiler barrel satisfactorily. The weigh shaft is therefore coupled to the countershaft midway between the axles. This has the usual outside arm and reversing rod to the cab. The particular example is applied to a 15-in. gauge model, but is representative of all similar cases in engines in smaller gauges.

The two designs of indirect link motion, i.e. a valve gear in which the motion is transmitted through a rocking shaft to valves on top of the cylinders as shown in Fig. 179, are interesting arrangements suitable for $\frac{3}{4}$-in. scale models and larger. Design "A" is the better one as it eliminates the careful fitting necessary in making and assembling the intermediate valve spindle, rocker and die-block used in design "B".

Gooch's Link Motion

In this motion the curved link, driven by the usual two eccentrics, is slung from the centre and is not moved up and down. The valve or radius rod is lifted or depressed by the reversing arm of the weight shaft, as in Walschaerts' gear.

Allan's Link Motion

This motion is a combination of Stephenson's and Gooch's motion. Both the link and the valve rod are connected (by opposite arms) to the weigh shaft. The link therefore moves one way and the valve rod the other, and by proportioning the lengths of the arms the expansion link can be made quite straight. The advance in Allan's and Gooch's motion is not effected by the angularity of the eccentric rods.

Walschaerts' Valve Gear *

The original reversing mechanism was invented by Egide Walschaerts, a Belgian locomotive engineer in 1844. A modified

* *Vide* "Walschaerts' Valve Gear," by Henry Greenly.

form of the motion was used by a German engineer, Heusinger von Waldegg in 1851. To-day Walschaerts' valve gear is used extensively in locomotive practice in this country.

In model work Walschaerts' valve gear is applied equally to slide or piston valve cylinders. In this connection it is important to note that, whereas for a slide valve arrangement the radius rod is connected to the combination lever below the valve rod, for a piston valve, with inside admission of steam, the radius rod is connected above the valve rod. Moreover, the setting out of the return crank on the coupled wheel also requires special attention: For slide valve cylinders this eccentric is set in advance of the crank pin, and for a piston valve scheme it is set in retard (Figs. 181 and 186 respectively).

Where Walschaerts' valve gear is employed between the frames, a separate eccentric takes the place of the return crank. The motion is used for inside and outside cylinders as follows—

CYLINDER ARRANGEMENT	VALVE GEAR ARRANGEMENT
Two Outside	Outside
Two Outside	Inside (G.W.R.)
Two Outside, One Inside	Outside and Inside.
Two Outside, One Inside	Conjugated
Two Outside, Two Inside	Outside and Inside
Two Outside, Two Inside	Inside (G.W.R.)

For admission of steam to the cylinder, full or partial valve travel is produced by the motion imparted to the return crank, eccentric rod, expansion link, radius rod and the valve spindle. The primary lap and lead movements, which are constant, are produced by the travel of the main crosshead, drop link, anchor link and the combination lever.

To exemplify the adaptation of the gear to a working model Fig. 181 illustrates a setting for a 1-in. scale engine with slide valve cylinders. The only difficulty that presents itself is that the lap employed in models is proportionately smaller than usual in full-size practice. The lower end of the vibrating lever moves to the extent of the piston stroke and it is difficult to get a small enough reduction in movement at the top joint. A setting out for a slide value is shown in Fig. 182. The vibrating lever is attached to the crosshead, and the bottom has a movement s and s_1. on either side of the centre. The lap of the valve L

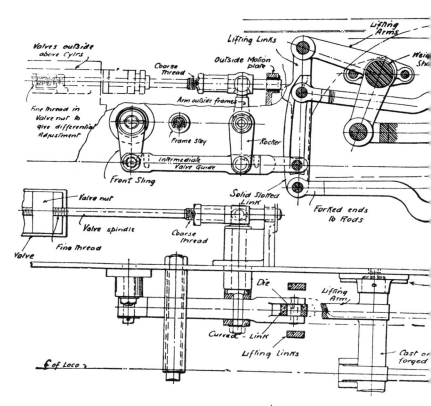

Fig. 177.—Inside link motion for "Atlantic"

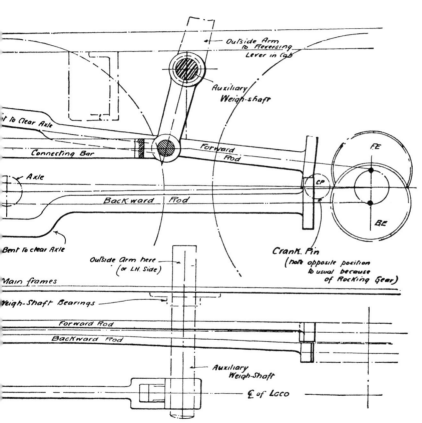

ocomotive with outside cylinders and valves.

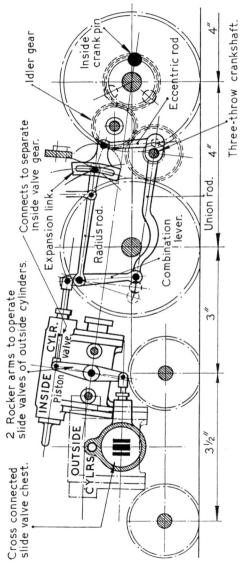

Idler gear

Inside crank pin

Eccentric rod

Connects to separate inside valve gear.

Expansion link.

Radius rod.

Combination lever.

2 Rocker arms to operate slide valves of outside cylinders.

INSIDE CYLR.

Piston valve.

Cross connected slide valve chest.

OUTSIDE CYLRS.

4″

Three-throw crankshaft.

4″

Union rod.

3″

3½″

Fig. 178.—Valve gear arrangement for 2½-in. gauge model of three-cylinder "West Country" locomotive.

[170]

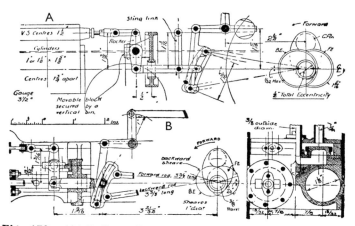

Fig. 179.—(A) Indirect link motion for 3½-in. gauge locomotive 1⅛-in. bore by 1⅝-in. stroke inside cylinders. (B) Indirect link motion with sliding guide rod and lever to operate valve rod.

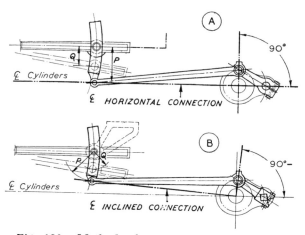

Fig. 180.—Methods of setting out eccentric rods for Walschaerts' valve gear.

must be equal to the movement L , and to obtain this the lengths of the vibrating lever v_1 and v_2 must be suitably proportioned. Now as the lap in a model is relatively small and the pins of the motion large this proportioning introduces mechanical difficulties. Means must therefore be devised to reduce v_2 to the minimum consistent with the strength of the parts. To provide for other sizes the author would recommend that the lap should not exceed half the width of the steam port. By using the longest possible vibrating link, a reasonable distance between the pivot pins may be obtained with a diameter of pin that will wear satisfactorily.

In the diagram Fig. 180A, the end of the expansion link coincides with the horizontal centre line of motion. The return crank is therefore exactly 90° from the crank pin. With an inclined eccentric rod the angle of inclination must be taken into consideration, as in B. The throw of the eccentric must be proportioned without regard to the function of the vibrating link, and, as in Stephenson's motion, must move the valve an amount equal to the lap plus the width of the port on each side of the centre. Of course the leverage (P and Q, Fig. 180) of the curved link must be taken into account as in the case of the ordinary Stephenson link.

The diagram (Fig. 186) shows the setting out of the gear for piston valve cylinders.

There are many variants of Walschaerts' valve gear. The Jones' gear is substantially the same as Walschaerts' but is designed to give variable lead to the valve. This is achieved by providing a further motion to the combination lever guided by the movement of the weigh-shaft lever.

Another interesting gear is the Deeley valve gear. This is substantially the same as Walschaerts' and is specially designed for inside cylinder locomotives. In place of the usual eccentric sheaves usually employed for inside Walschaerts' or Stephenson's, the eccentric rod operating the valve of one cylinder takes its motion from the connecting rod of the second cylinder—it being 90° out of phase with the other—and vice versa. The motion is transmitted to the expansion link as in the case of the usual Walschaerts' gear, complete with combination lever.

In addition to Walschaerts' gear, the Baker valve gear is also widely employed on locomotives in the U.S.A. The two gears are similar in their respective setting out except that the

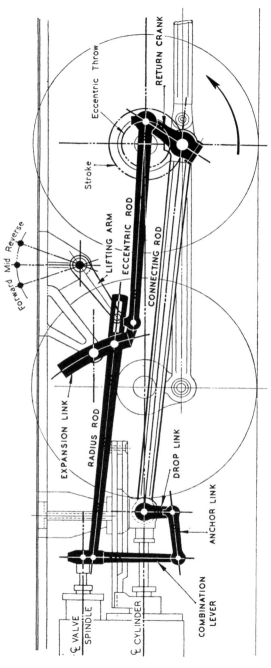

Fig. 181.—Diagram of the essential parts of Walschaerts' gear for slide valve cylinders.

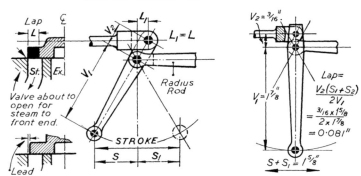

Fig. 182.—The setting out of the "lap and lead" functions for vibrating lever of Walschaerts' gear. L_1 travel of valve to the extent of lap and lead. $S + S_1$ equal the stroke of the piston.

Fig. 183.—Walschaerts' gear: Detail of combination lever for small model. (For slide valve only.)

$$Lap = \frac{V_2(S_1+S_2)}{2V_1}$$
$$= \frac{3/16 \times 15/8}{2 \times 17/8}$$
$$= 0·081''$$

latter employs a combined system of levers which transmit the required valve travel through a form of bell crank to the main valve or radius rod. The displacement of one set of levers by adjustment of the weigh shaft from the cab varies the cut-off and direction of rotation as required.

Box (Expansion) Links

In Walschaerts' gear the box form of construction is to be

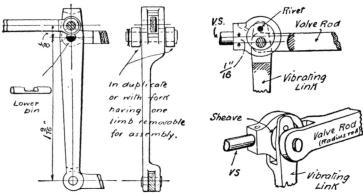

Fig. 184.—Assembly of combination lever to radius rod and valve rod.

recommended. The two curved plates (left and right hand) are turned to form the central pivot pins. Care has to be taken in the machining of the grooves for the die block and the top and bottom distance pieces. The expansion link is assembled complete with the bottom extension piece to suit the eccentric rod pin joint. This latter joint is set back a small amount to ensure equal swing of the box link and to give balanced port openings. (Dimension "B" Fig. 197.)

Joy's Valve Gear

This form of the original "Hackworth" radial valve motion became very popular in the latter part of the nineteenth century. The great advantage claimed in real practice is that it clears

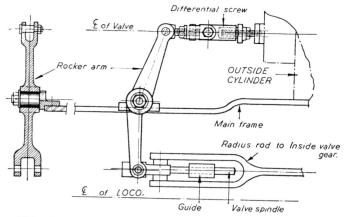

Fig. 185.—Arrangement of rocker arm for transmission of motion from inside gear to the outside cylinder valve spindle.

the already cramped crank shaft of the four eccentrics, and in model work this characteristic is the most valued one. With inside cylinders the valves must, in the smaller gauge models, be placed above or below the cylinders, and Joy's valve gear, or one of its modifications, therefore makes a convenient and simple reversing gear.

In employing the driving crank pin, or a point on the connecting rod, to actuate the valve, the function of the vertical

[175]

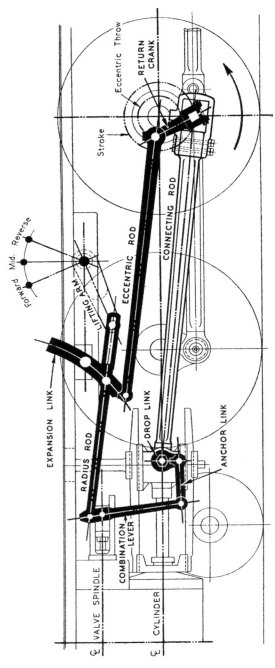

Fig. 186.—Diagram showing the essential parts of Walschaerts' gear for piston valve cylinders.

(Photo: Courtesy K. N. Harris, Esq.)

Fig. 187.—Piston valve cylinder arrangement and Walschaerts' valve gear. (Note the assembly of the radius rod to the top pin joint of the combination lever.)

movement is to open the port and, in the combination of this motion with the horizontal component of the crank-pin circle, an "advance" is obtained, as in the case of the combination of the eccentric (or return crank) and crosshead movement in Walschaerts' valve gear. If the valve motion in Joy's gear were taken directly from a point in the connecting rod, the joint

Fig. 187a.—Detail of return crank assembly for 15-in. gauge locomotive designed by the author.

pin would follow a path in the form of a more or less perfect
ellipse. But while this would, as shown by the diagram (Fig. 188)
at A B and C D, give an equal port opening, at the dead centres
(see E F) there would be a serious error. The top joint E, which
represents the die or slide block in the tilting slide shaft, would
not occupy its proper central position owing to the loss in the
height due to the angle at which the vibrating link stands when
in the dead centre position.

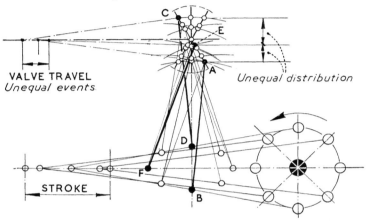

Fig. 188.—Diagram showing the travel of valve, motion taken
from a point on the connecting rod. The base of the vibrating
link AB travels in an elliptical path. The displacement of the
top joint from A to C causes unequal valve travel.

In Joy's gear the system of links employed corrects this
error. The vibrating link is attached to a lower link (called a
jack link) slung from the connecting rod. The anchor link at
the lower end of this can be of any length, and is simply a
convenient attachment. The horizontal position of the weigh
shaft is determined by the ellipse formed by the point on the
connecting rod, the maximum angle of the weigh-shaft being
not more than 30° from the vertical.

The length of the correcting or "jack" link will be determined
by the position of the connecting rod in respect to the rail
level, but the length of the vibrating lever must be such that,
when an arc the length of the proposed vibrating lever is swung
to the vertical centre line, as in Fig 189, then $A = A_1$. This can

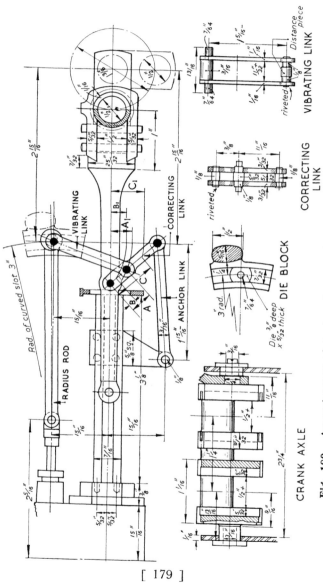

Fig. 189.—Arrangement of Joy's valve gear for 3¼-in. gauge model locomotive.

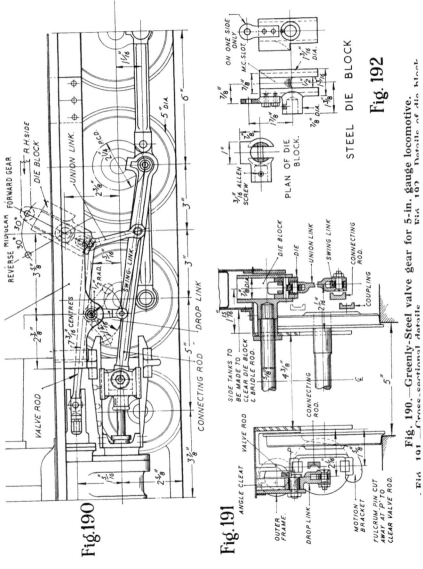

Fig. 190.—Greenly-Steel valve gear for 5-in. gauge locomotive.

Fig. 191.—Cross-sectional details.

Fig. 192.—Details of die block.

STEEL DIE BLOCK

Fig. 192

Fig. 190

Fig. 191

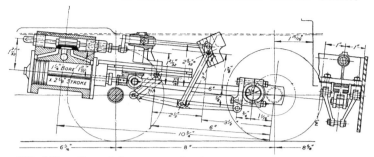

Fig. 193.—Greenly's corrected valve gear for inside cylinders.

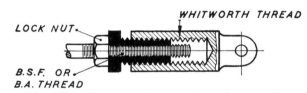

Fig. 194.—Compound screw for valve spindle.

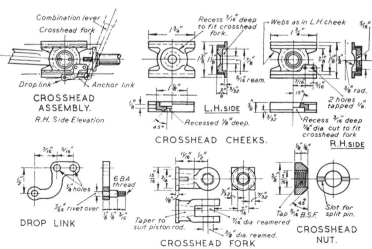

Fig. 195.—Crosshead for 5-in. gauge inside cylinder.

[181]

be found by a trial and error method on paper in a few moments; both B B_1 and C C_1 do not equal each other, and are attempts which do not realize the above condition obtaining in the length marked A.

In the design of Joy's motion the lap and lead function is derived from the horizontal motion of the vibrating lever through the medium of an eccentric top pin. As the extent of the motion in Joy's gear is always less than in Walschaerts', it is possible in most examples to employ two separate pins. The lower pin, which extends through on each side to the slide blocks, may be cut through to about half its diameter to reduce the distance between centres. This scheme is shown as an alternative at A (Fig. 189), and if adopted the lap of the valve will be slightly larger than that used with the eccentric pin device. A curved slide should be employed with this type of motion in large engines, especially in conjunction with an early maximum cut-off.

Greenly's Corrected Motion for Inside Cylinders

The author has devised a form of correcting motion which has been arranged to suit all normal designs. It has the merit of giving a sufficiently accurate correction and provides for joint pins of almost any diameter. Joy's gear, when modelled on a small scale, is rather small in this respect and therefore is not recommended.

The motion is derived from a point on the connecting rod near the big end. At this point a swing link is jointed to a lug by a substantial pin. The other end of the swing link is supported by a correcting link, the point near the centre forming the connection to the vibrating lever. The function of the correcting link is not only to carry the swing link, but to lift it at each dead centre to the exact amount required to neutralize the loss in height of the vibrating link due to the latter's angularity when in this position. The setting out is best done graphically, as the various links at first may work out awkwardly regarding their relation with other parts of the engine. The pivot point on the connecting rod being fixed, a point on the swing link should be chosen that will lift the die block sufficiently to open the valve fully when the link is inclined at not more than 30°. With the big end on dead centre and the vibrating link swung to its utmost, as shown in Fig. 193, the line S L, representing the

[182]

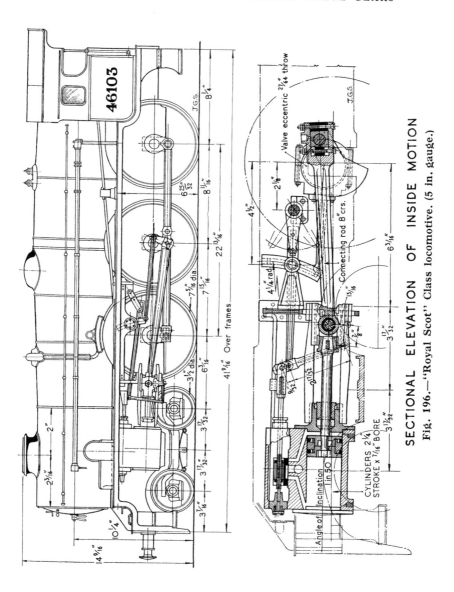

SECTIONAL ELEVATION OF INSIDE MOTION

Fig. 196.—"Royal Scot" Class locomotive. (5 in. gauge.)

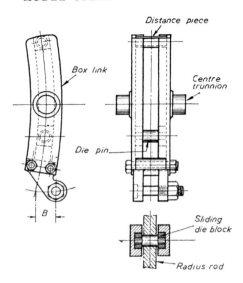

Fig. 197.—Walschaerts' valve gear. Expansion link for 10¼-in. gauge model locomotive.

Fig. 198.—Arrangement of weigh shaft for Walschaerts' valve gear on 2½-in. model 2–10–4 locomotive.

swing link, should be drawn in, cutting the lower point L. Farther along this link a point must be chosen for the correcting link. The length and pivot point of this is chosen, the necessary function being that, in swinging, the lower end shall lift to coincide with the points.

One feature of the author's designs of this and Joy's valve gears is the use of straight slides in the shaft, the slides being formed by drilling the solid casting and afterwards sawing and filing (or milling) the spaces between. The slides themselves are pieces of bright mild steel rod. With a long valve rod (radius

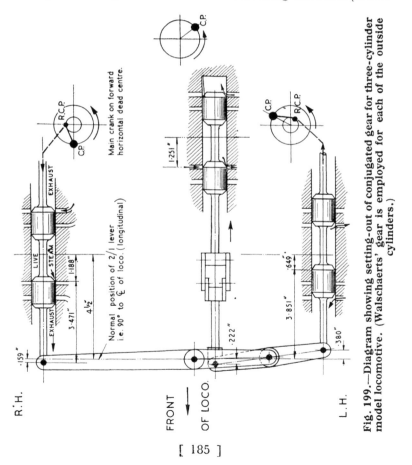

Fig. 199.—Diagram showing setting-out of conjugated gear for three-cylinder model locomotive. (Walschaerts' gear is employed for each of the outside cylinders.)

rod) and small lap the straight slide has little effect on the steam distribution, and can safely be used in models up to $1\frac{1}{2}$-in. scale. In small models the scheme is much to be preferred to the usual device of allowing the extension of the top pin of the vibrating lever to work in grooves in the slide shaft. An example of the gear is shown in Fig. 193.

Greenly's Corrected Valve Gear for Outside Cylinders

A combination of levers has been devised which provides a very sound and realistic valve gear for locomotives with outside cylinders and valves on top. It is arranged to take its motion from the crank pin, and the weigh shaft and correcting link are supported from an outside girder-frame of exactly the same style as the girder used for carrying the Walschaerts' motion employed on engines of the "Pacific" and 4–6–0 types.

The gear in a one-inch scale model is more robust than Walschaerts' and, furthermore, involves fewer parts and joints. The method of setting out is the same as for the inside-cylinder motion, but the swing link that it is found convenient to employ is very much longer. The drawing (Fig. 190) shows an arrangement of the gear. In larger models the lap (advance) function is obtained with an eccentric or twin-head connection to the vibrating lever as in other types of radial valve gears. The enlarged view of the slide shaft shows that it is made up of two blocks or castings cross-connected by a shaft running in bearings in the main frame (Fig. 191).

Tests for Radial Valve Gears

In setting a radial gear the ultimate test for accuracy is to place the connecting rod *exactly* on dead centre. The valve rod should not move either way on the reversing lever being shifted from one extreme to the other. If it moves with the reverse rod the die is too high, and an opposite movement shows that it is too low. The axleboxes may also be out of position vertically, and the spring nuts (a relatively strong spring is advisable on the driving axle) may be adjusted either up or down. The valve is then adjusted on its spindle to give equal port opening and admission. Time of admission is more important than that of the cut-off or the precise amount of maximum port opening.

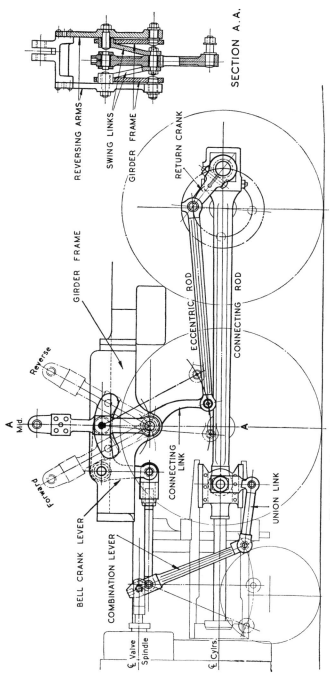

SECTION A.A.

REVERSING ARMS

SWING LINKS

GIRDER FRAME

RETURN CRANK

GIRDER FRAME

ECCENTRIC ROD

CONNECTING ROD

Reverse

Mid.

A

Forward

BELL CRANK LEVER

CONNECTING LINK

UNION LINK

COMBINATION LEVER

Valve Spindle

Cylrs.

Fig. 200.—Baker valve gear for American 4–8–4 model locomotive.

Valve Adjustments

Means for a fine adjustment in the position of the valve on the spindle is a valuable asset, especially if such adjustment can be effected without taking any part adrift when under steam.

The differential screw system is perhaps the best, and is exemplified by the illustration (Fig. 194). Here a nipple with a coarse thread is screwed into the intermediate valve spindle, the spindle having a fine thread. A rotation of the nipple gives a finer adjustment because of the difference in the pitch of the two threads.

Conjugated Gear (Gresley Gear)

For three-cylinder locomotives, two sets of outside Walschaerts' gear may be employed with a lever system linking them together in such a way as to impart the valve motion to the inside cylinder. Details of the lever system as set out for a $7\frac{1}{4}$-in. gauge three-cylinder model locomotive are shown by Fig. 199. This method, as defined by Mr. H. Holcroft*, is based on the principle that when two harmonics with different phases are combined, a third harmonic with an intermediate phase is produced.

Indirect Valve Motions

For outside cylinders with inside valve gears, as described in Chapter VIII, p. 132, provision has to be made for transmitting in phase the motion to the valve spindle. Fig. 185 shows standard G.W.R. practice as applied to a $1\frac{1}{2}$-in. scale model. (*See also* Fig. 2). Under these conditions, the respective cranks must be set 180 degrees apart.

A further development for model valve gear is shown in the setting out, Fig. 178. Provision is made for three sets of inside gear; one of them acting directly upon the valve spindle of the inside cylinder as shown. The other two sets of gear operate the respective inside valves of the outside cylinders through a rocker arm. Details of the outside cylinders are shown in Fig. 135 (Chapter VIII).

---

* "Conjugated Valve Gears for Locomotives: Their History and Development", by H. Holcroft. "The Engineer", Feb. 15, 1946, p. 145.

CHAPTER XI
MOTION DETAILS

Connecting Rods for Inside Cylinders

THE connecting rod in the simpler models generally resolves itself into a modification of the marine type with a split big end. These are usually cast in gunmetal, the ends sawn, soldered and bored for the journal and screws, and then unsoldered. The length of an inside-cylinder connecting rod varies from $3\frac{1}{4}$ to 4 times the stroke. The size of the small end pin should not be less than the diameter of the piston rod.

A type of rod which better imitates the orthodox strap-ended rod is illustrated in Fig. 202. This particular design is provided with a lug for a valve gear lever. The strap is fitted before boring the bearing, and the sides of the big end are faced on a mandrel. The rod portion is usually cleaned up and painted, the ends being bright.

An example of the strap-ended rod in a more elaborate form is shown in Fig. 203. Both ends are fitted with adjustable brasses and the straps are secured by two bolts in each case. A strapped little end is usually employed in conjunction with a four-bar crosshead.

Where a model is too small to fit safety-lock screws to the cotter, the latter should have a very slow taper. Marine big ends were sometimes employed in real practice as illustrated in Fig. 204. The steel forging for the rod has a forked end and split brasses. The latter are secured in the fork by a lipped cap of steel and two substantial bolts.

The little ends of inside-cylinder locomotives are usually of the eye-ended pattern, bushed with a plain brass bush. On the G.W.R. the forked little end is, however, a standard fitment on a large number of inside-cylinder locomotives.

Connecting Rods for Outside Cylinders

Where the cylinders are outside the frames a connecting rod of good appearance, finish and accuracy to scale is an essential. The smaller model has rods either of mild steel or

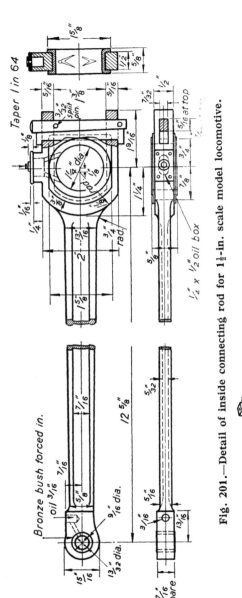

Fig. 201.—Detail of inside connecting rod for 1½-in. scale model locomotive.

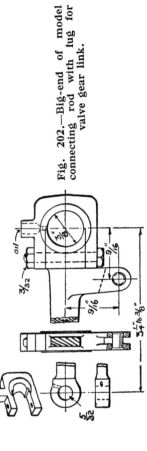

Fig. 202.—Big-end of model connecting rod with lug for valve gear link.

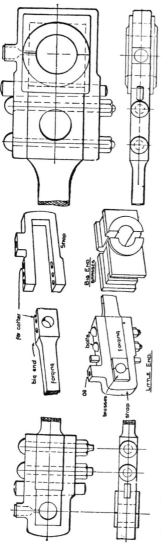

Fig. 203.—Details of big ends with straps for connecting rods. (Inside-cylinder locomotive.)

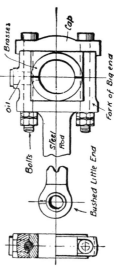

Fig. 204.—Connecting rod with marine-type big end.

(*Photo: V. B. Harrison, Esq.*)

Fig. 205.—Arrangement of outside motion for No. 1 gauge 2-6-4 tank engine. (Greenly Engineering Models, Ltd.)

aluminium alloy. It is imperative to a good model that the big end, at least, should be bushed with phosphor-bronze. The little end of a steel rod may be case-hardened only and should work on a hardened pin.

The ordinary rectangular big end may be modelled very satisfactorily by turning a bronze bush with a square outside flange and secuing this with a cotter pin in the connecting rod as illustrated in Fig. 206.

A G.N.R. type of big end for a connecting rod is shown by Fig. 207. The rod is forked, and a block is bolted in the open end of the fork after the split "brasses" have been inserted. A cotter with two safety set-screws provides for the adjustment of the split bearing brasses. The particular design is taken from one of the older engines. In later and larger examples the proportions are increased to suit a larger crank-pin.

Fig. 208 shows how the bearing brasses may be adjusted by a wedge block or gib actuated by a screw. It is not a very common arrangement, but is quite good.

A connecting rod with a marine-type big end is shown in Fig. 209.

For a large model the author has designed a big end as shown in Fig. 210. The rod is made from a steel casting, complete with flutes, the end being of the box form. The brasses are

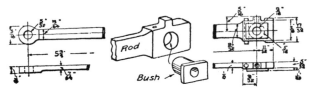

Fig. 206.—Simple connecting rod for small model.

[192]

split, the rear one being lipped over on the inside on one edge only, the cotter holding the front brass in a lateral direction. To increase the amount of oil carried, a hole is drilled at A and sealed by a removable screw cap bolt. The horizontal hole needs plugging up permanently on the outside. The lubricator on top carries a little thick oil, or preferably grease which would melt if the big end tends to overheat.

For an engine of similar size a forged rod with a marine-type big end is provided. The bolts in this case are relieved in the centre so that a passage is formed for the oil from the lubricator. The little end is bushed with bronze.

Crossheads

These are somewhat troublesome items in model loco-motive construction, and in their making good workmanship will well repay any extra time spent on them. They are designed mainly in three forms—for one, two or four slide-bars respectively. In large models the two-bar system, which is perhaps the most used, may have a crosshead cast in steel or gunmetal of the form shown in Fig 211. The pin should be hardened, and as the fitting of a small flat cotter may be considered difficult the piston rod should be secured with two or more standard taper pins driven into carefully reamered holes. More than one taper pin is absolutely essential to maintain the strength of the fixing, and three taper pins fairly close together are nearly as effective as a flat cotter in resisting shear stresses.

As it is not always possible to get a satisfactory cored casting the recess for the little end must be provided for in other ways. The crosshead may be machined from a piece of steel bar and have separate slippers attached to them, as shown in Fig. 212, by soldering or brazing.

Very small models may be fitted with crossheads having one side wall only, the pin being overhung. Crossheads for $2\frac{1}{2}$-in. gauge locomotives made in this way are illustrated in Fig. 213. For inside cylinders $\frac{3}{16}$-in. slide bars are employed in this size, and the crossheads are cast end to end in pairs in gunmetal or machined out of flat steel bar. Mild steel bar is usually employed for outside slide bars, as it is often very desirable to reduce the thickness of the crosshead to a minimum to provide for the side movement of the bogie wheels.

N

[193]

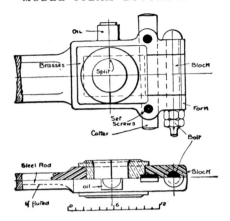

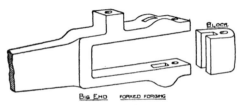

Fig. 207.—Connecting rod big end for G.N.R. model locomotive.

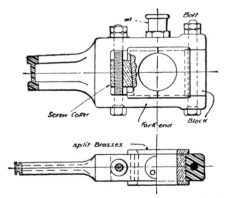

Fig. 208.—Box type end of connecting rod with screw and wedge adjustment for the split brasses.

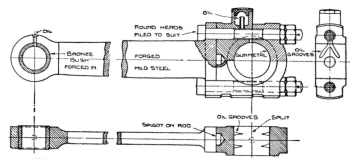

Fig. 209.—Connecting rod with marine-type big end.

The forked little end will require a crosshead of a design similar to that shown in Fig. 214. Here the pin moves with the connecting rod and takes a bearing in the crosshead. If made of steel the latter should be bushed with phosphor-bronze.

A typical four-bar crosshead is illustrated in Fig. 190 (see Chapter X). In a very large model separate slide blocks would be used in place of the one-piece crosshead shown in this drawing.

The single-bar crosshead is used on some railways. A typical design is illustrated in Fig 215. Various other types of slide bars are often modelled by employing round rods, the crossheads being drilled to suit them. The tubular slide bar may also be employed where the cylinders have cylindrical stuffing boxes

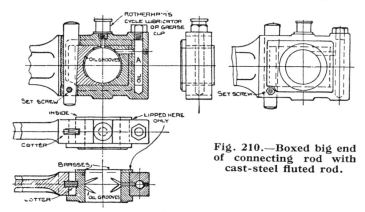

Fig. 210.—Boxed big end of connecting rod with cast-steel fluted rod.

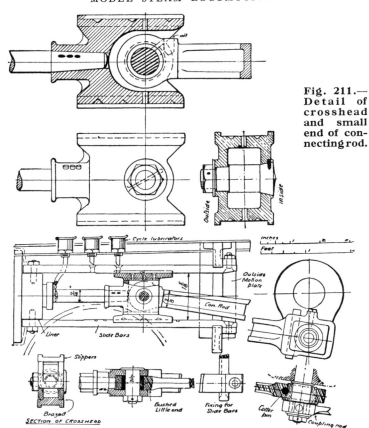

Fig. 211.—
Detail of
crosshead
and small
end of con-
necting rod.

Fig. 212.—Arrangement of outside motion for small 1½-in.
scale model locomotive.

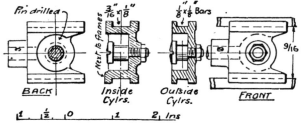

Fig. 213.—Crosshead for 2½-in. gauge model.

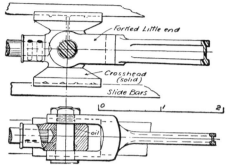

Fig. 214.—Crosshead with forked connecting rod.

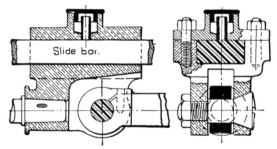

Fig. 215.—Crosshead for single slide bar.

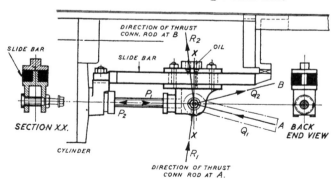

Fig. 216.—Crosshead and overhead slide bar for model locomotive. (It will be noted that when the engine is moving forward, the crosshead exerts an upward thrust against the bars. The intensity of the load varies according to the position of the crank.)

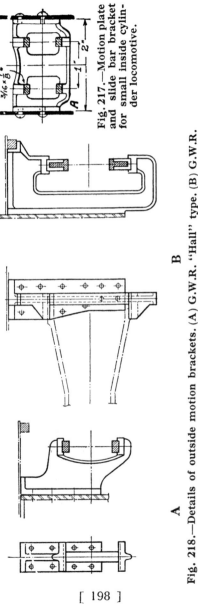

Fig. 217.—Motion plate and slide bar bracket for small inside cylinder locomotive.

Fig. 218.—Details of outside motion brackets. (A) G.W.R. "Hall" type. (B) G.W.R. "King" type.

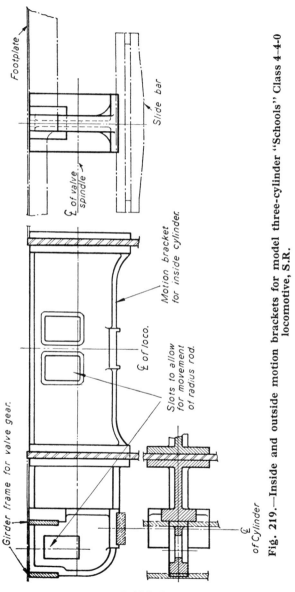

Fig. 219.—Inside and outside motion brackets for model three-cylinder "Schools" Class 4-4-0 locomotive, S.R.

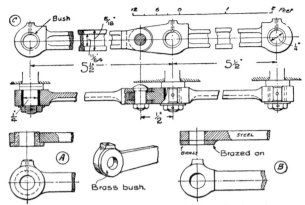

Fig. 220.—Details of model coupling rods.

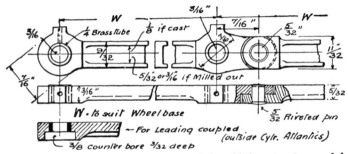

Fig. 221.—Details of coupling rod for 2½-in. gauge model.

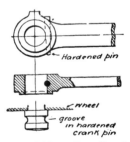

Fig. 222. — Detail of
retaining pin for
small model coupling
rod.

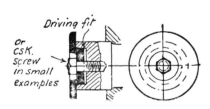

Fig. 223.—Detail of retaining cap
for crank pin.

[200]

and no other provision for fixing the bars. In such cases a separate socket is often made to hold the bars, and then, complete with the bars, pushed on to the cylindrical stuffing box. Fig. 216

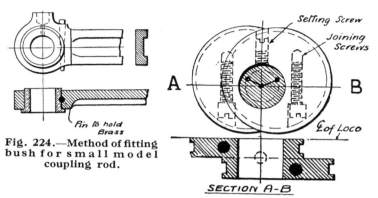

Fig. 224.—Method of fitting bush for small model coupling rod.

SECTION A-B

Note : Patterns must be .R.& L.H.

Fig. 225.—Detail of eccentric sheaves cast in pairs.

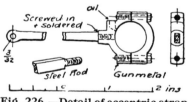

Fig. 226.—Detail of eccentric strap for small model.

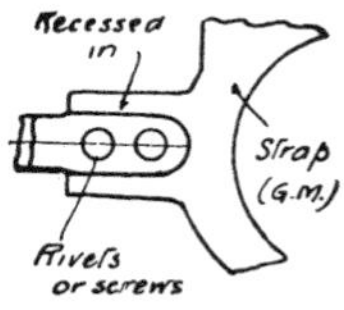

Fig. 227.—Method of fixing small eccentric rod to strap.

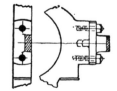

Fig. 228.—Method of fitting eccentric rod to strap for large model.

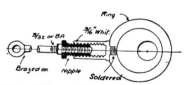

Fig. 229.—Adjustable eccentric strap and rod.

[201]

shows a modification of an orthodox pattern of crosshead provided with a slotted slide-bar. The direction of the arrows indicates the loads the crosshead and slide-bars are subject to for two positions of the connecting rod.

Motion Plates

The illustrations (Figs. 217 and 218) are typical of those employed for inside- and outside-cylinder engines respectively.

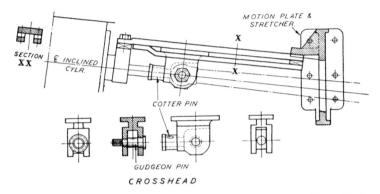

Fig. 230.—Assembly of slide bars and crosshead for inside cylinder
L.N.E.R. "Pacific" locomotive.

They, in all cases, need modification to suit the disposition and dimensions of the particular form of valve gear and motion adopted. In the normal engine with a leading bogie it will be found necessary to allow plenty of clearance for the bogie wheels and frames. The special pattern of outside bracket is necessary in some forms of six- and eight-coupled engines, and is sometimes made up of plate material as a pierced or "spectacle" plate.

The forked pattern of bracket is perhaps the best, but in some cases the characteristics of the prototype require a motion plate of the style shown in Fig. 219. It is also convenient to provide lugs or bosses on the upper edge to carry footplates.

Slide Bars

The general practice is to carry slide bars from the rear-cylinder cover and lugs are cast on the motion plate. When slide bars only measure $\frac{1}{8}$ in. or $\frac{3}{16}$ in. wide the fixings require modification. In small scale practice the arrangement shown in Fig. 125, Chapter VIII, is employed, the slide bars being screwed to a flange formed on the cylinder cover. When secured in this way the function of the motion plate is to prevent the bars spreading.

Coupling Rods

For small models coupling rods are made in an aluminium

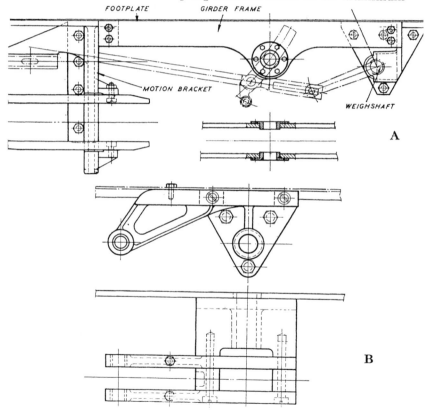

Fig. 231.—(A) L.M.S. type of girder frame for valve gear. (B) L.N.E.R. cantilever type of combined weighshaft and expansion link bracket.

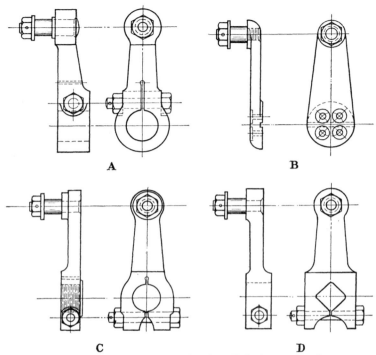

A   B

C   D

Fig. 232.—Typical return cranks for Walschaerts' valve gear.

alloy or mild steel. In all larger models, rods should be bushed with bronze bushes. For small engines the scheme A, Fig. 220, is quite good and saves quite a lot of work in dealing with the rod. The arrangement at B is common, but more or less of an imitation. For six- or eight-coupled engines it is necessary to joint the rods to allow for the vertical movement of the axle-boxes when the engine is standing on a surface that is out of level. The usual method is shown in Fig. 220 (c). Fig. 221 illustrates an alternative method.

The "Pacific", 4–6–0 and other types of outside-cylinder locomotives with leading coupled wheels must be provided with a specially thin retaining nut, one form being illustrated in Fig. 84, Chapter VI. For very small models a countersunk-headed crank pin, or the device shown in Fig. 222 is sufficient. For a large locomotive the author uses the design shown by

Fig. 223. The arrangement for securing the bush in an ordinary pattern of coupling rod end, shown in Fig. 224, is also a good one. Coupling rods should be measured off from the centres of the wheels after the latter have been fitted to the frames.

Where the rods are jointed, as in the case of a six- or eight-coupled engine, all the joints should be made and fitted up before the holes for the crank pins are marked out and drilled. When this is done one pair of wheels (the drivers for preference) should be secured to their axle at the appropriate angle to one another. The coupling rods should then be fitted on the crank pins and the other wheels secured in their positions without removing the rods. The latter act as a jig, and if the crank pins are all at the correct throw and are fitted quite squarely into their wheels the rods should rotate quite freely without binding at the "dead-centre" positions.

Eccentrics and Straps

Where the eccentrics are not turned solid with the shaft and, as arranged in Fig. 179, have to take up a position between the adjacent crank webs of the axle they may have to be cast in pairs and split, as shown in Fig. 225. The screws are fitted after splitting and the sheaves are then turned on a suitably centred mandrel. Cast iron or mild steel should always be used for the sheaves. Straps are best made of bronze bar or cast gunmetal. The lugs should be long, so that the bolts may lie close to the sheave. Figs. 226 to 228 show various methods of fixing the eccentric rods. Of course, in very small engines with slip or single eccentrics the strap and rod may be cast in one piece, the strap not being split, or a ring may be turned out of the solid bar with a round rod fixing in the manner shown in Fig. 229, which provides a differential screw form of valve adjustment at the same time.

In small engines eccentric sheaves are often grooved in the centre and a rib formed on the bearing surface of the strap to freely fit this groove. This reduces the overall size of the sheave, which is important where they are cut solid with the axle.

In large engines, and where this consideration may not apply, the groove is best arranged in the sheave. The double-flanged sheave, shown in Fig. 225, is not often used. By adopting the central rib or groove method just described, the dimensions of overall width can be cut down to the minimum.

[205]

CHAPTER XII
BOILER CONSTRUCTION

Simple Boilers

THE type of boiler fitted in toy models in which the flame of the lamp impinges on the lower outside surface of the barrel is usually made of thin copper. The ends are flanged over the barrel and the whole is secured with a good grade of solder. Such boilers are quite safe up to a pressure of about two atmospheres (30 lb.), and, as already stated, owe their steaming power to the thin metal (No. 24 I.W.G.), of which they are made and to the fact that a spirit lamp burns best in natural draught. Details of the method of construction are shown at A in Fig. 233. There are limits to their usefulness and, therefore, for all home-made models using direct-acting slide-valves cylinders made up from castings, other systems of boiler construction providing greater heating surface are essential.

Water-tube Boilers

The water-tube type of boiler is one which fulfils the requirements of many model locomotive builders, and since it can be made up without brazing or silver-soldering is undoubtedly the simplest and safest method of construction. Fig. 235 shows a 2½-in gauge inner boiler made up with screwed or spun joints caulked with soft solder. The barrel should be a piece of fairly stout copper tube; normally, No. 20 s.w.g. material is quite strong enough, but for this particular purpose No. 18 gauge would be advisable. The ends should be turned true and the inside surface skimmed to a taper, as detailed at B, Fig. 233. A stout copper plate (No. 14 s.w.g.) is then turned with a taper edge and a driving fit in the tube. The surfaces should be tinned with soft solder, and after fitting together the taper edge of the tube should be spun over the end with a burnisher. The water-tubes are fitted into screwed elbow-sockets, back nuts being employed to secure steam tightness at the joints. The sockets at the rear end must be provided with

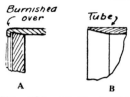

Fig. 233.—Method of fitting boiler ends for small models. All joints silver-soldered.

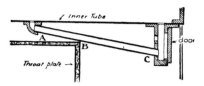

Fig. 234.—Detail of water-tube boiler construction for small model.

sufficient length of thread to allow of fixing by the running-joint method, the tube being screwed in farther than required, so that the front sockets can be introduced into the boiler tube.

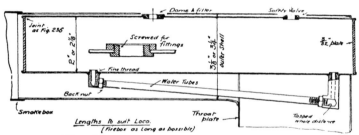

Fig. 235.—Simple type water-tube boiler.

By using fine threads soft solder will be found to securely caulk all joints. A longitudinal stay is not required where the inner boiler barrel is under 3 in. diameter unless a proportionately thinner end than that shown is used.

As mentioned in Chapter IV water-tube boilers in a larger gauge can be made on similar principles, a cast upcomer and downcomer being arranged to receive the tubes. The downcomer at the back end would be fitted with a door, so that the tubes can be expanded

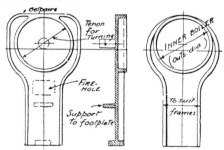

Fig. 236.—Cast back plates for small model boilers. Belpaire or roundtop types.

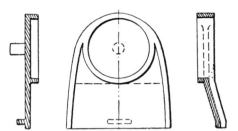

Fig. 237.—Back and throat plates for the
Wootten type boiler with wide firebox.

in or fixed with a running screw joint as desired. The critical
point in setting out the tubes is at the throat plate.

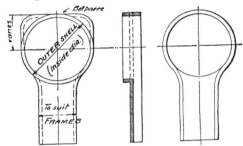

Fig. 238.—Throat plates for narrow fireboxes.
(Belpair or round-top boilers.)

The tubes between A and C must just clear at point
B, Fig. 234. The use of inclined or curved throat plates
will assist matters in this connection.

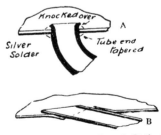

Fig. 239.—Methods of fitting
water tubes.

For front ends of water-tube
boilers flanged spinnings out of
the same thickness of metal as
the barrel may be used and
are quite satisfactory, especially
if slightly dished. They should
be a tight fit in the tube, and if
properly silver-soldered need
not be otherwise secured. For
the back plates gunmetal
castings $\frac{1}{8}$ in. thick are com-

monly employed. These are made in either of the shapes shown in Figs. 236 and 237, and have flanges to carry the outer shell. Water tubes are fixed either by silver-soldering or brazing, this work being accomplished at the first heat when fixing the front end. The cast back plate must be run with a finer solder (a silver-solder with a lower melting point) than that used for the copper parts. Back plates for both "Belpaire" and round-topped boilers may be made from castings. The flange supporting the outer casing should, in an unlined boiler, be finished as thin as possible at the top, so that the inner boiler nearly touches the outer shell at this point. This is important. Where a piece of drawn tube is employed for the outer shell it is not always possible to obtain enough length of metal for the sides of the firebox out of the tube itself; therefore

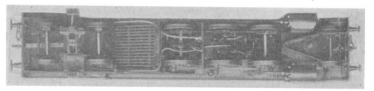

(Photo : V. B. Harrison, Esq.)

Fig. 240.—Underneath view of a coal-fired No. 1 gauge 2–6–4 tank locomotive.

cast throat plates are used as shown in Fig. 238. Such are essential in the "Belpaire" type, as a separate wrapper plate for the firebox must be used. The same applies to the "Wootten" firebox plates which are illustrated in Fig. 237. The shell of a boiler with a round-topped firebox may be rolled up out of a flat sheet, the barrel and firebox wrapper being made out of the same piece. This method of construction eliminates the cast throat plate, the latter being a piece of sheet metal brazed into the saw cut.

Fig. 239 shows two methods of fixing tubes. The first (A) is used at either the front or the back, while the second (B) is often adopted at the former point. The hole is drilled and then elongated to suit the tube by inserting and bending over a piece of steel rod of the same diameter as the tube.

In all soldering work absolute cleanliness must be observed at all joints. All oxides must be removed by scraping. When silver-soldering is to be followed by soft-soldering pickling for a few hours in a 5% solution of sulphuric acid, warming the

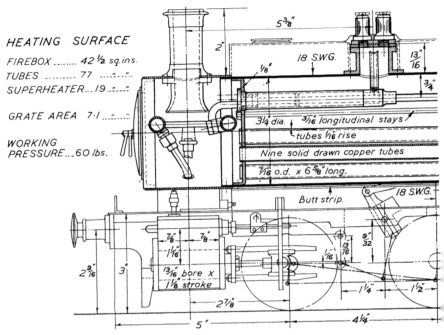

HEATING SURFACE

FIREBOX .... 42½ sq. ins.

TUBES .... 77 .....:....".

SUPERHEATER... 19...:...:

GRATE AREA 7·1 ...:....:

WORKING
PRESSURE...60 lbs.

Fig. 240a.—Design for 3½-in. gauge

work to hand-heat before plunging, in addition to the scraping is essential. The work in either soft- or hard-soldering must not be raised to a temperature much above that of the melting point of the solder used. This is important in using tinman's solder, as it is so easily "burnt" and the surfaces oxidized and rendered unclean. When this happens the scraping process will again be necessary and the parts require re-soldering together.[1]

Water tubes which are not screwed should be made of a lighter gauge, consistent with strength, for improved heat transfer. Solid-drawn (seamless) copper tube should be specified.

Where the outer shell is of tapered construction the inner tubes may be either stepped or coned.

[1] Brazing temperatures are 1,400° to 1,500° Fahr, ⎫ Flux, for both, Borax
Silver solder   ,,   ,, 1,100° to 1,130° ,, ⎭
Tinman's ,,   ,,   ,, 380° to   550° ,,   Flux, Zinc Chloride

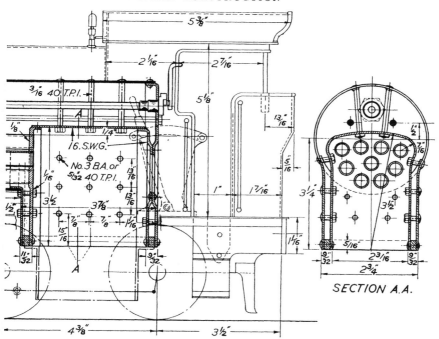

industrial type saddle tank locomotive.

As the difficulty in small boilers is to provide enough air space and water capacity, the form of boiler shown in Fig. 52, Chapter IV, but with the addition of water tubes, could be employed. This type of boiler can be used in conjunction with the plain spirit wick or vaporizing lamp, and for this reason the good natural draught and more or less perfect combustion of the fuel when the locomotive is either standing or running are both obtained without the least complication.

For all water-tube boilers it is essential that the inner barrel should not be too large, or of too heavy a gauge. The outer shell may be thick and made of sheet steel, lined with asbestos in a single thickness. Downcomers have no great value in the evaporation of water, and should only be used where more convenient from a constructional point of view, as shown in Fig. 234.

Loco-type Multitubular Boilers

The orthodox locomotive type boiler comprises the main steam barrel fitted to an internal firebox located at the rear end of the engine. The distance between the main locomotive frames usually governs the size of the firebox, but in the case of "Atlantic", "Pacific", articulated and special types of locomotives, wide fireboxes can be fitted. The furnace is fitted with the usual fire grate and ashpan below. The combustion gases are carried away from the firebox through a number of flue tubes to the smokebox at the front end. The walls and crown of the furnace, together with the flue tubes, provide the all-important heating surface.

The assembly of parts that make up a complete boiler unit and the location of internal fittings have to be designed and set out with a view to their ultimate fixing and subsequent accessibility for repairs and overhaul.

In its simplest form the small solid-fuel boiler can be fitted with a single flue tube, but is not very efficient and not to be recommended. Nearly all the valuable heat passes down the core of the tube to the smokebox instead of being conducted through the tube wall to the water. The efficiency can be raised to a limited extent by inserting cross water tubes in the firebox or one or more longitudinal water tubes in the main flue tube, provided there is sufficient space available.

Small Boilers

The multitubular scheme is the one that is universally employed in model locomotive practice. A working model of this type can be built in $1\frac{3}{4}$ in. gauge provided special attention is given to design and construction. One with a wide firebox is to be preferred and fitted with $\frac{3}{8}$ in. diameter copper flue tubes. The furnace tubes should be of comparatively light gauge—No. 20. All flat sides of the firebox must be stiffened by an adequate number of stays. The firebox is built up by silver soldering the plates together, the foundation ring being riveted. The boiler barrel, which should be made from solid-drawn copper tubing to the appropriate British Standard Specification, is prepared for the flanged end plates. The front end of the barrel is riveted to the smokebox barrel, which is fixed to the saddle. The firebox end must be allowed longitudinal movement due to thermal expansion, otherwise, if held rigidly, it would

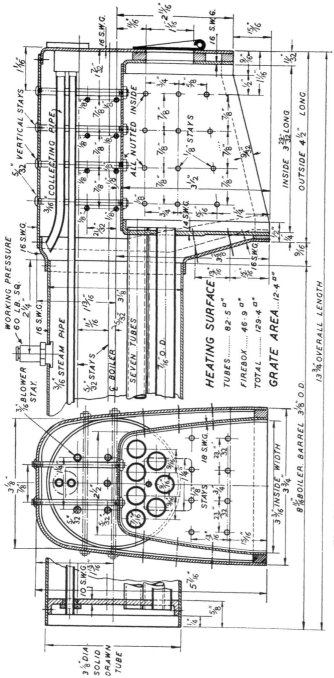

Fig. 241.—Coal-fired boiler for 2½-in. gauge locomotive with wide firebox.

Fig. 242.—Small solid fuel boiler under construction.

buckle and distort. Axles adjacent to the grate should be suitably protected by a cover plate or casting.

Specification for 1 Gauge Boiler

Boiler Barrel.—$2\frac{1}{4}$ in. solid drawn copper tube. No. 18 s.w.g.
Firebox.—Outside—No. 16 s.w.g. copper sheet. Inner—18 s.w.g. copper sheet. No. 16 s.w.g. end plates.
Flue Tubes.—$\frac{5}{16}$ in. outside diameter copper No. 20 s.w.g. (6 or 7).
Stays.—Direct screwed copper, $\frac{1}{8}$ in. diameter, 40 t.p.i.
All joints subject to steam pressure silver soldered.
Steam pressures 40 to 45 lb. per square inch, gauge.

Fig. 243.—Construction of large coal-fired boiler with Belpaire firebox and sloping grate.

[214]

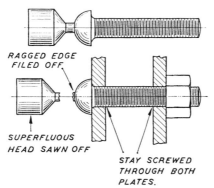

RAGGED EDGE
FILED OFF.

SUPERFLUOUS
HEAD SAWN OFF

STAY SCREWED
THROUGH BOTH
PLATES.

Fig. 244.—Method of screwing stays
in small boiler.

The use of a "dry back" boiler is recommended for small
gauge models of narrow firebox generators. The added surface
of water space is negligible in such small engines and a larger
firehole is thus made possible.

The author's arrangement for a $2\frac{1}{2}$-in. gauge solid-fuel boiler
of the wide firebox type is shown in Fig. 241. The barrel may
be $3\frac{1}{8}$-in. or $3\frac{1}{4}$-in. diameter, and seven tubes $\frac{7}{16}$-in. diameter
will be found to give satisfactory evaporation. The back plate,
front tube, throat plate, and in some cases the firebox tube
plate, require sound gunmetal castings. Leakage due to the
porosity of poor castings used for various flanged plates is an

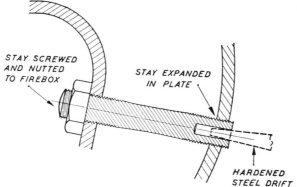

STAY SCREWED
AND NUTTED
TO FIREBOX

STAY EXPANDED
IN PLATE

HARDENED
STEEL DRIFT

Fig. 245.—A Method of fixing screwed roof stays.

[215]

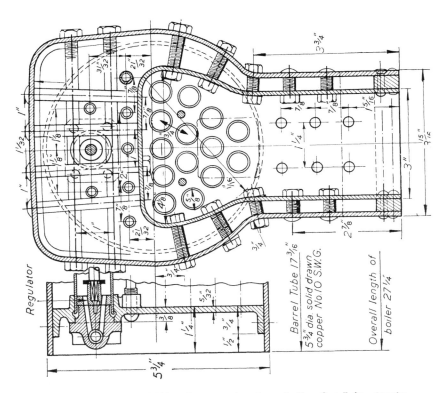

Figs. 246a and 246b.—Locomotive-type boiler for 5-in. gauge G.W.R. "Hall" class, with Belpaire fire-box.

[The original model was fitted with a smokebox-type superheater. By rearranging the tubes, provision can be made to fit two larger tubes for return-bend superheater elements. (See Fig. 292.)]

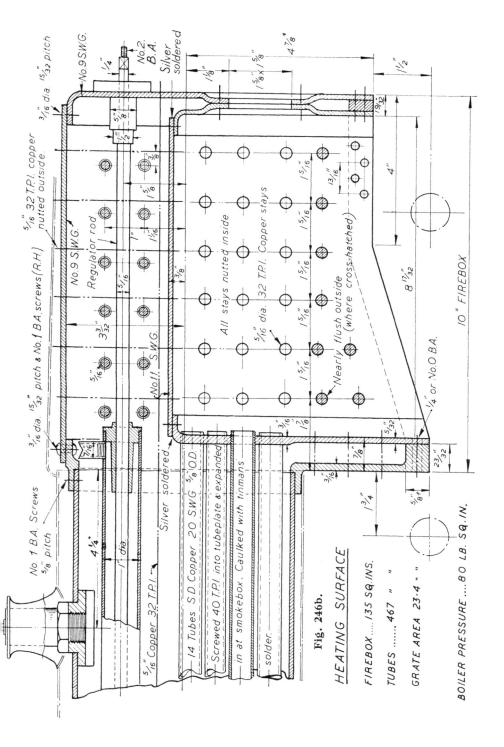

Fig. 246b.

HEATING SURFACE

FIREBOX......135 SQ.INS.

TUBES ......467 " "

GRATE AREA 23.4 " "

BOILER PRESSURE....80 LB. SQ.IN.

Fig. 247.—G.C.R. locomotive boiler in copper with castings in gunmetal.

annoying kind of failure—one which is not usually discovered until the boiler is finished—the castings should be carefully hammered all over before machining or filing to size. Recourse can be made to tinning the castings all over before assembling to lessen the risk of porosity. But the tinning process cannot be resorted to for any parts that require to be silver soldered afterwards. The use of solid-drawn copper tube is recommended for the barrel, and both the spigot of eth throat plate and the

Fig. 247a.—Assembly of fittings on boiler with wide firebox.

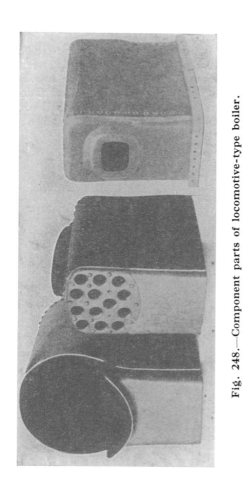

Fig. 248.—Component parts of locomotive-type boiler.

Fig. 249.—Locomotive boiler parts.

circular front end should fit the barrel tightly. The joints of the firebox must be silver-soldered throughout, sufficient screws or rivets being used in the flanged joints to hold the parts together during this operation. The wrapper plate of the outside firebox may then be riveted and soft-soldered to the throat plate, all joints being drawn up quite tightly.

The firebox tube plate having been previously screwed for the tubes the complete inner firebox unit (see Fig. 242) may be fitted into the shell, the wrapper being riveted, or screwed where rivets are impossible, to the back plate. The foundation ring is made up of copper strip carefully fitted and riveted with $\frac{3}{32}$-in. copper rivets. The tubes are fitted last. They are screwed

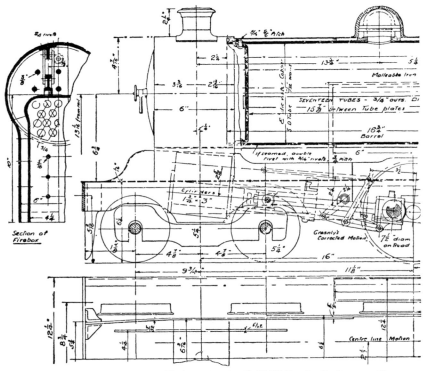

Fig. 250.—Design for 7¼-in. gauge L.N.W.R. tank locomotive. Inside cylinders 1¾-in. bore by 3-in. stroke. Coupled wheels 7½-in. diameter. Boiler pressure: 70 lb. per sq. in. Tractive effort: 68 lb.

40 T.P.I., slightly tapered, and on being soft-soldered will remain tight under all conditions. The front ends are quite satisfactory if carefully expanded and soft-soldered. Other methods of fixing tubes are shown by Fig. 252. Where snap-head rivets cannot be used, and, as in an unlagged boiler, the surface must be quite flush and cleanly finished, countersunk screws may be used; the countersinking being only half the usual amount, the screws can then be filed flush.

The keynotes in the construction of small copper loco-type boilers are, clean plates, good fitting joints, secure riveting or screwing, and screwed fittings all being caulked with soft solder. The main joints of the inside firebox, because of the possibility

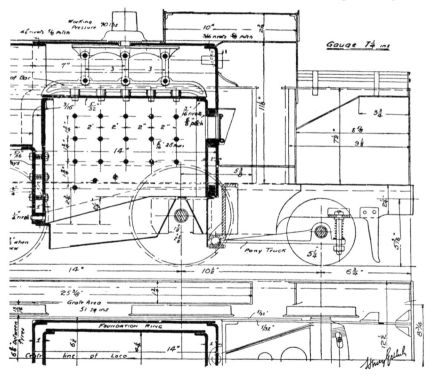

Fig. 250a.—(See Illustration on preceding page.)

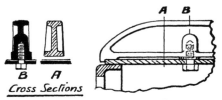

Fig. 251.—Girder roof stays for crown of firebox.

mission to a considerable degree, tubes, and every part which heating surface should not be any thicker than the dictates of safety would suggest. Suitable wooden former blocks can be prepared and the whole of the plates, more especially of the inner firebox, flanged by hand. A casting may be employed for the firebox tube plate, as it provides thicker metal in which to form the screw threads for the tubes. There is no reason, however,

of the water level falling below the crown, should be silver-soldered. (For the inner shell of a water-tube generator brazing and silver-soldering only is recommended.) As thin plates help the heat transmission, inner firebox plates, can be considered as efficient

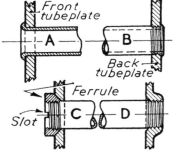

Fig. 252.—Methods of securing flue tubes.

why the tube plate holes should not be flanged inwards, to ensure a sufficient number of threads for securing the tubes.

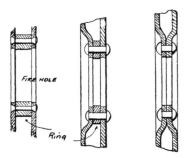

Fig. 253.—Details of fireholes in back plate of boiler.

Large Boilers

Larger boilers for $\frac{3}{4}$-in. and 1-in. scale locomotives can be made up from the sheet copper and riveted in the orthodox manner when solid drawn copper tube is not available. As such boilers are always lagged, rivet heads are left showing. Non-ferrous metals are always employed up to $1\frac{1}{2}$-in. scale. Steel boilers with plates not less than $\frac{3}{16}$ in. thick are commonly made for locomotives in $9\frac{1}{2}$ in. gauge and upwards. The steam tightness of steel boilers depends on secure riveting and corrosion (or "taking up") of the plates touching one another. Tubes are always expanded in and steel tubes give the best results. Of course, the heating surface is reduced if the rather more coarsely constructed steel boiler is employed instead of the thinner copper one, and the author has therefore, for his most successful engines up to $9\frac{1}{2}$ in. gauge, employed copper throughout. The $7\frac{1}{4}$-in. gauge models of the L.M.S.R. "Royal Scot" and G.C.R. locomotive boilers, built to the author's design by Messrs. Bassett-Lowke, Ltd. are excellent examples of this construction. If this material is adopted, it is better to rely on the use of soft solder for caulking than attempt to get steam tightness by the use of the caulking tool. In a small steel boiler the tinier "weeps" of water which may be many and usually appear even on the final hydraulic test can usually be stopped by a washing out of the whole boiler with a solution of sal-ammoniac. In copper boilers it is important that all fittings and fixtures in contact with the water should be non-ferrous.

Typical designs of large model loco-type boilers are given by Figs. 246 to 248. The components of the ordinary boiler with

Fig. 254.—2–8–2 type goods locomotive with large boiler and wide firebox.

[223]

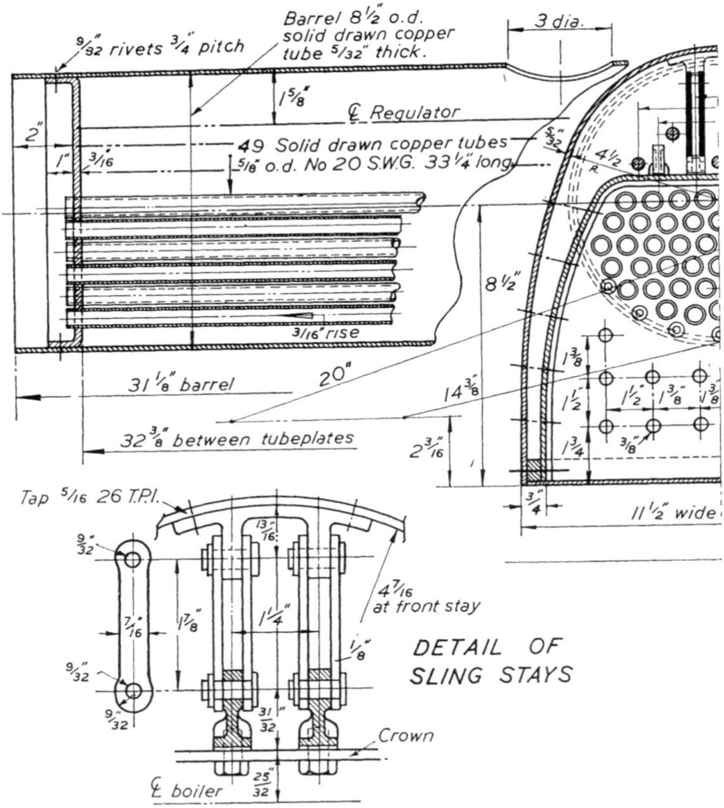
Barrel 8 1/2" o.d. solid drawn copper tube 5/32" thick.
9/32" rivets 3/4" pitch
3 dia.
1 5/8"
℄ Regulator
2"
1"
3/16
49 Solid drawn copper tubes 5/8" o.d. No 20 S.W.G. 33 1/4" long
5/32"
4 1/2 R.
8 1/2"
3/16" rise
31 1/8" barrel
20"
14 3/8"
32 3/8" between tubeplates
2 3/16"
1 3/8"
1 1/2"
1 3/4"
1 1/2"
1 3/8"
3/8"
3/4"
11 1/2" wide
Tap 5/16 26 T.P.I.
9/32"
13/16"
7/16"
1 7/8"
1 1/4"
4 7/16 at front stay
1/8"
DETAIL OF SLING STAYS
31/32"
Crown
℄ boiler
25/32"

Figs. 255a and 255b.—Boiler with wide firebox for 7¼ in. gauge "Pacific" type locomotive.

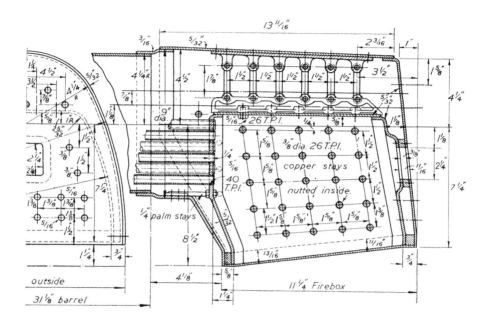

TOTAL EVAPORATIVE HEATING SURFACE ..... 2980 SQ. IN.

GRATE AREA .... 100 SQ. IN.

BOILER PRESSURE ...... 85 LB. SQ. IN.

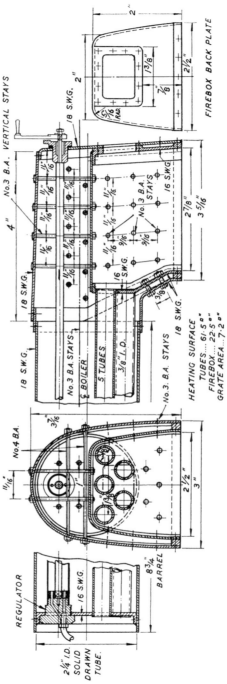

Fig. 256.—Coal-fired boiler for No. 1 gauge L.N.E.R. type "Pacific" locomotive.

a round firebox are shown in Fig. 248. The plates at the throat in this type may be set out either as shown at A or B (Fig. 249). With the "Belpaire" firebox the throat plate extends to the top as shown at C. It is because the throat plate takes this form that a casting is so convenient in small-gauge models (see Fig. 238). In any case, whether the plate is flanged out of sheet material or cast the boiler barrel will have a square end, as at A, and the firebox wrapper, which is not notched (see B), will be bent over a flat-topped wooden former to suit the square head portion of the throat plate (C). The boiler (Fig. 250) for a model 4–4–2 type tank locomotive of $7\frac{1}{4}$ in. gauge may be made in copper or steel. Copper plates $\frac{3}{32}$ in. or steel $\frac{3}{16}$ in. thick would be employed, with possibly a $\frac{3}{16}$ in. firebox tube plate in either case. The barrel, failing the supply of 8 in. solid drawn tube, would be made up of the plate material and riveted with a lap seam with rivets in two rows. For a steel boiler the rivets would not be less than $\frac{1}{4}$-in. diameter, and a butt seam might be used if the plates were first acetylene-welded, the strip being placed on the outside. Larger rivets are always required where a caulking chisel is used. The boiler illustrated has a roof supported by a girder. This is slung from a T-bar riveted or bolted on to the wrapper. The total area of the rivets or bolts used should be sufficient to safely support the crown with a factor of safety of at least 10.

Wide or "Wootten" Fireboxes

In view of the large capacity, grate area and number of tubes to be obtained by employing the well-known "Wootten" firebox a considerable amount of skill has been shown by free-lance designers of model locomotives in arranging the frames and wheels in such a way that the largest and deepest firebox the loading gauge will allow is provided.

Increased efficiency may be obtained by introducing water tubes in the firebox. They are introduced to improve end-to-end circulation and take water from a point towards the front end of the barrel and deliver it at a convenient point above the crown of the firebox.

Stays

It is vitally important that all flat and curved plates in boilers should be adequately supported and strengthened by means of stays. Firebox side stays are fitted to prevent the inner and outer plates bulging and collapsing due to the stresses induced. These stays may also be subject to indeterminate bending stresses due to thermal expansion of the plates.

Screw stays made from hard-drawn copper having an ultimate tensile strength of 14·5 tons per square inch or bronze rod to the desired B.S. Specification should be used. Holes are tapped straight through the inner and outer plates in one operation. A long tap is required for this purpose. The stays are caulked

(*Photo: J. R. Jeffress, Esq.*)

Fig. 257.—Assembly of boiler on chassis of 4–8–4 American loco-motive.

with soft solder, the inside ends being nutted. A nick in the rod should be just deep enough to allow the stay to break off when screwed home and the end riveted (Fig. 244).

Girder stays may be employed to support the firebox crown of a round top boiler. In a large model these require to be secured to the outer wrapper. For small boilers the girders may be built up of angle or tee sections. Special cast girder stays screwed to the crown are employed for larger boilers. The firebox crown should be slightly rounded for stiffening. For "Belpaire" fire-boxes, flat surfaces are essential to successful fitting of rods and stays. The corners of the boxes should be well rounded.

Longitudinal stays numbering two or more are fitted end to end, care being necessary to ensure that the nuts clear the various boiler fittings at the respective ends. Palm stays are employed to

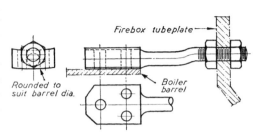

Fig. 258.—Detail of boiler palm stay.

secure the firebox tube plate and can be riveted to the main barrel. Tubular stays are fitted in small models to be used as a steam supply pipe for the blower in the smokebox end. In large boilers working at comparatively high pressures —where the total loads acting on the plates as a whole can be measured in tons—gusset stays are employed in the design.

Fabricated crown roof stays made of copper plate formed into **C** or **I** sections and riveted in position are sometimes employed. If this method is adopted, care must be taken to arrange for adequate riveting and silver-soldering of the joints. The plates themselves must also be strong enough to withstand the distributed loads covering the flat surfaces.

Fireholes

These should always be much larger than the scale equivalent of the prototype for convenience in firing.

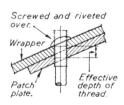

Fig. 259.—Detail of boiler patch plate for stays to give increased effective depth of thread.

The rectangular type is also much to be preferred, with a drop-down door. As shown in Fig. 253, the plates may be pressed out to obtain a joint, with or without an intervening ring. There is, however, not always sufficient width for this in narrow fireboxes, as the bends of the plates occupy a certain amount of room. For charcoal-fired engines the opening should be quite near to the top of the box, as this fuel must be heaped up.

[229]

Brick Arches

The purpose of a brick arch in the firebox is to deflect the high-temperature gases away from the tubes and tube-plate. The effect is also to induce more complete combustion of the fuel. The arch should be constructed of a suitable refractory material capable of withstanding temperatures of the order of 2,500° F. A thick steel plate, that can be renewed when necessary, can be used as an arch for 1-in. scale models if desired.

Hydraulic Test

A hydraulic test is carried out on a boiler (and other thin pressure vessels) for the purpose of assessing the strength of all parts under stress. The test must be undertaken before the boiler is subject to steam pressure and is usually of the order of one and a half times to twice the normal working pressure. It is completely filled with warm water and connected to a suitable hydraulic pump unit. The pressure is increased gradually and in stages of 10 or 20 lbs. per sq. in. At each stage the boiler is inspected for leaks and failures. The maximum pressure is held for about ten or fifteen minutes. Extra pumping may be found necessary during this period in order to make up for unavoidable leakages and weepings.

It is important to note that when the boiler is subject to the extreme pressure all parts are being strained (stretched) and therefore the stresses induced should still be well within the ultimate value for the material; leaving a good margin of safety, otherwise permanent set of the material will occur and upon the release of pressure it will not recover. For this reason, tests should be carried out by an experienced engineer.

CHAPTER XIII

BOILER MOUNTINGS, CAB AND OTHER FITTINGS

Safety Valves

In modern locomotive practice the Ramsbottom duplex safety valve has been superseded by the "pop" valve. The Ramsbottom is very much larger and the range of pressure between blow-off and shut down is greater (A ratio of 5 to 1 compared with the "pop" type).

It is not advisable to make a working model of the Ramsbottom valve for locomotives of a scale of less than $\frac{3}{4}$ in. to the foot, and even then it is difficult to get a satisfactory tight valve unless the lever has the jointed front pivot as indicated in Fig. 260 at A. The use of a lever with the two fixed points. i.e. both being integral with the lever, does not allow the valves to find their proper seatings naturally and leakage is the result. Sometimes the spring is of the tension type, but the compression spring shown is to be preferred.

Where the Ramsbottom valve is not enclosed in a casing a small model may be made to closely represent the actual thing by using one valve only, as illustrated in Fig. 261. The working spring is hidden inside the cab. The device is then virtually the same as the spring-balance safety valves largely used during the nineteenth century, the M.R. standard pattern (Fig. 262), placed on top of the dome, being the best known.

Where the valve is hidden by an ornamental casing the model-maker can make what alteration he pleases to the working parts so long as the exterior outlines are preserved. Fig. 263 shows a simple direct-loaded valve which has an easing lever fitted to the spindle. The exterior design is quite representative of a cased Ramsbottom valve.

In all models up to $3\frac{1}{2}$ in. gauge one valve, so long as it is a good one, is ample. The diameter of a valve can be determined according to the data in Table XI, adjustments being made according to the circumstances of the case.

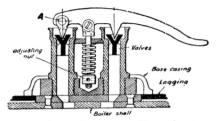

Fig. 260.— Open-type Ramsbottom
safety valve.

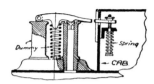

Fig. 261.—Dummy Rams-
bottom type of safety valve
with loading spring hidden
in cab.

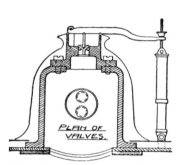

Fig. 262.—Old Midland Railway type of safety valve on
dome.

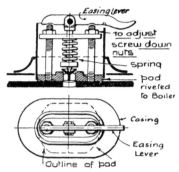

Fig. 263.—Simple safety valve
of the direct-loading type fitted
with Ramsbottom casing.

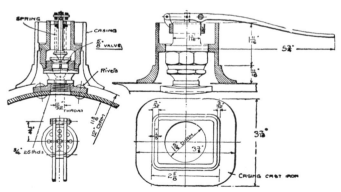

Fig. 264.—Safety valve for model 2-in. scale (9½-in. gauge).
Great Northern Railway "Atlantic" locomotive.

TABLE XI

SAFETY VALVE ORIFICES

(E. A. Steel)

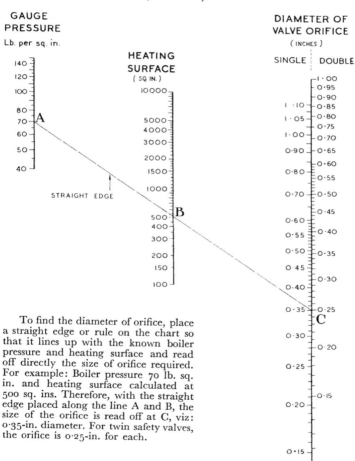

To find the diameter of orifice, place a straight edge or rule on the chart so that it lines up with the known boiler pressure and heating surface and read off directly the size of orifice required. For example: Boiler pressure 70 lb. sq. in. and heating surface calculated at 500 sq. ins. Therefore, with the straight edge placed along the line A and B, the size of the orifice is read off at C, viz: 0·35-in. diameter. For twin safety valves, the orifice is 0·25-in. for each.

(Nomogram compiled by J. Greenly Steel)

[233]

The data is based on the formula—

$$d = k \sqrt{\frac{H}{P}}$$

Where

d = diameter of orifice, inches.

H = heating surface, square inches.

P = boiler pressure, lb. per square inch (absolute).

k = a constant, viz.: 0·129 for a single valve of the "pop" type, 0·092 for twin valves of the "pop" type, 0·163 for a valve of the Ramsbottom type.

The direct-loaded valve enclosed in a cylindrical casing is an excellent type. Its application inside the casing of a different type of valve is shown in Fig. 264, which is taken from the author's set of designs for a 2-in. scale G.N.R. "Atlantic" engine. The prototype has two Ramsbottom valves side by side. The arrangement provided for the twin levers which are, in the model, loosely connected to the spindle of the valve so that they act as easing levers.

A valve designed for a smaller model is illustrated in Fig. 265. The parts of this valve consist of (a) a bushing which should be either screwed and soldered or silver-soldered to the boiler shell, (b) a valve seating with a knife-edged orifice, (c) the valve made of hard gunmetal or nickel, (d) an outer casing screwed on to the seating made of tube, (e) the spring, (f) the pointed spindle which should apply the load into a recess in the top of the valve, and (g) the adjusting cap to the casing. The last named is drilled with a number of holes for the passage of escaping steam.

A "pop" action (an accelerated discharge of the valve) can be obtained by making the head of the valve nearly fit a cylindrical recess in the seating (b). The steam will then act on a larger area as soon as it is released, and the valve will lift quickly and to a visible amount. By experiment the leakage area referred to in the drawing may be so adjusted that the valve shuts as suddenly as it lifts, with only a few pounds' loss in pressure between rising and falling. The "pop" valve works better with dry steam, and in order to prevent priming and upsetting its action the throat of the valve orifice may be restricted as indicated in the valve shown in Fig. 264. The head of the valve should not be too large, and where two valves are employed

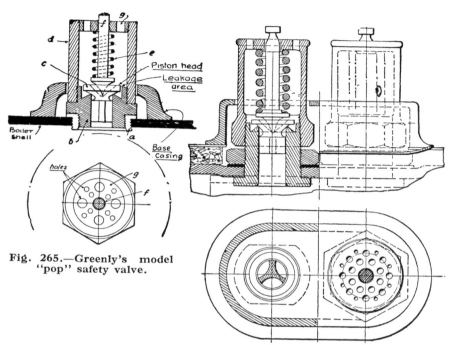

Fig. 265.—Greenly's model "pop" safety valve.

Fig. 266.—Direct loading type twin safety valve for large model.

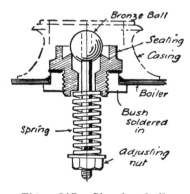

Fig. 267.—Simple ball safety valve with internal spring.

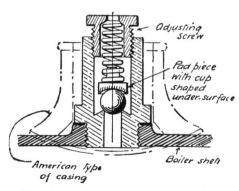

Fig. 268.—Simple ball safety valve with external spring.

they should be rather smaller than usual, one being set at a slightly lower pressure than the other.

The author has made successful "pop" valves as small as $\frac{3}{16}$ in. diameter. The G.W.R. type of casing shown in Fig. 269 is perhaps the simplest and neatest for enclosing a "pop" or other similar type of cylindrical valve.

As nothing is so annoying than a continuously leaking safety valve, model-engineers should take care to see (1) that the valve is turned truly round and fits the seating freely, (2) that the seating is of the knife-edged variety and is true, (3) that the pressure of the spring spindle is *delivered to a point on the valve below the level of the seating,* and (4) that the spring spindle is quite separate and not a part of the valve except where the valve is of spherical shape.

A direct-loaded twin valve for a large model is shown in Fig. 266.

Bronze and stainless steel balls may be used as safety valves. Two methods are illustrated (Figs. 267 and 268). In the first (Fig. 267) the ball is screwed and soldered on to a spindle, the bronze wire spring being inside the boiler. This is perhaps the only satisfactory type of internal spring safety valve, a variety which is sometimes necessary in a small-scale model. In the other valve (Fig. 268) the ball is pressed down on to a knife-edged seating by a spring pillar having a rounded under-surface. This makes a very good valve. In both cases the seating is trued by hammering on it a steel ball of the same diameter as the bronze ball. Grinding-in cannot be resorted to.

To obtain steam tightness with the ordinary V-seated valve grinding-in must be carefully done. Emery should not be used with brass valves; grindstone-mud is much to be preferred. Further, the part of the seating in contact with the valve should never be much more than ·01 in. wide, in model locomotives of small size.

Domes

Domes are used in actual engines to provide space for the extraction of the steam from a point high up above water level. As a rule, in large engines the regulator is fitted inside the dome. This is not always practicable in a small model, therefore the dome simply houses the end of the pipe leading to the regulator valve, and further provides a ready means of filling the boiler.

Domes should always be double-cased, the outer ornamental covering being made from a stamping or spinning or turned from a casting. In modern engines the dome is more squat than those on older locomotives, due to the restrictions of the loading gauge, and the use of high-pitched boilers of larger

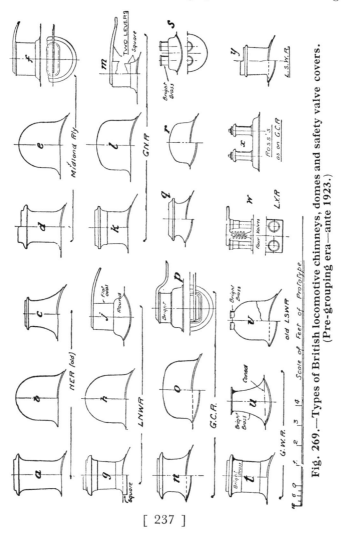

Fig. 269.—Types of British locomotive chimneys, domes and safety valve covers. (Pre-grouping era—ante 1923.)

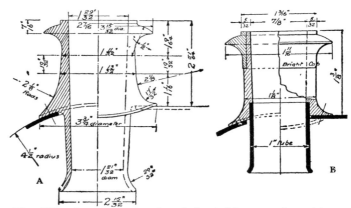

Fig. 270.—Internal extension of short chimneys: A, cast type
and B, tubular type.

diameter. The diagram (Fig. 269) illustrates a few of the earlier
designs.

Chimneys

The scientific importance of the locomotive funnel has
already been discussed in Chapter IV. In this country the
engineer generally attempts to give the funnel an ornate character
and some of the distinctive shapes are illustrated in the diagram.
Where a free-lance design of model is being built, a proportion
in which the smallest diameter of the stalk is in a ratio of 1
to $3\frac{3}{4}$ to that of the smokebox on which the chimney rests will
be found to give a good appearance. Built-up chimneys are
usually distinguished by the joint lines across them, cast-iron
ones usually being quite plain; and while a chimney may taper

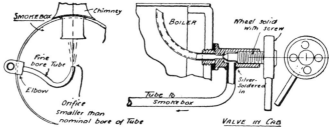

Fig. 271.—Arrangement of steam blower for No. 1 gauge
model.

either way on the outside the internal diameter always tapers outwards towards the top. Short chimneys are usually extended down into the smokebox to make up for their deficiency in apparent height. This extension in a model may be cast with the funnel or, in small engines, consist of a short length of tubing, as at B in Fig. 270.

Cab Fittings

These vary considerably with the size of the model. The smallest (No. 1 gauge) engine with a spirit-fired boiler may be used with no fittings other than a regulator, but a pressure gauge and a steam blower are very convenient and useful fittings. Working pressure gauges on the Bourdon principle are made as small as $\frac{3}{4}$-in. diameter, and if obtained with a reading 50% more than the maximum pressure used will remain accurate for a long time. Such gauges must not be overloaded and, further, must be fitted on a U or syphon pipe to protect the mechanism from the heat of the steam. A try-cock may be added,

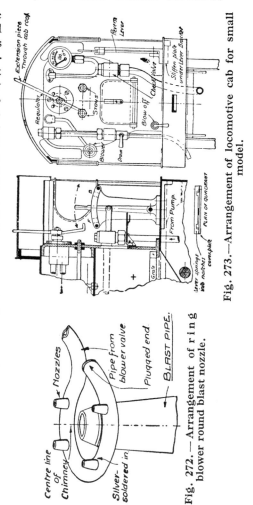

Fig. 273.—Arrangement of locomotive cab for small model.

Fig. 272.— Arrangement of ring blower round blast nozzle.

but, if used, a screw-down type should be chosen in preference to the common plug-cock. In small sizes especially plug-cocks soon leak and seize.

Steam Blower

For a solid-fuel boiler a steam blower is an essential part of the equipment and the simplest arrangement is shown in Fig. 271. The steam is taken from the dome (or the highest point in the boiler) and is controlled by a screw-down valve. The steam is conducted to the smokebox and emerges from a fine orifice. A fault with such blowers is that the orifice may be so large that the boiler will not make steam against its consumption. In a $2\frac{1}{2}$-in. gauge model, the hole should not be more than $\frac{1}{32}$-in. The blower should be low down in the smokebox alongside the blast pipe and delivering a jet as nearly central in the chimney as possible. The blower steam supply may be conducted through a hollow longitudinal stay in the boiler. In large models a ring of jets are arranged to encircle the blast pipe orifice (Fig. 272).

In some cases it is possible to introduce the blower pipe and jet into the centre of the blast pipe. This can be arranged in cases where the exhaust pipes are of the inverted Y pattern, used in many outside-cylinder locomotives.

Fig. 274.—Cab fittings for $2\frac{1}{2}$-in. gauge model locomotive.

Fig. 275.—Cab fittings for $1\frac{1}{2}$-in. scale, Great Central Railway model locomotive.

TABLE XII
BLOWER JET ORIFICES

Scale of model inches	diameter of orifice inches	No. of orifices
$\frac{17}{32}$	·031	1
$\frac{3}{4}$	·050	1
1	·031	3
$1\frac{1}{2}$	·050	4
2	·062	4

Water Gauge

For large solid-fuel models, or in locomotives with the orthodox loco-type boiler a water gauge is essential. The internal bore of the passages and glass should be at least $\frac{1}{8}$ in. or $\frac{5}{32}$ in.

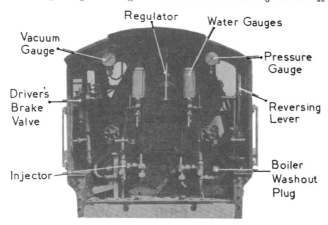

Fig. 276.—Cab interior of 15-in. gauge locomotive.

to prevent capillary attraction causing a false reading of the water level. The simple type of water gauge (Fig. 282) is recommended. As in the case of the larger patterns, one with a blow-down valve or cock is an improvement.

Reversing Gear

Reversing gear fitments in the cab will depend on the type of valve motion used. For a hand-controlled gear two devices

Q

[241]

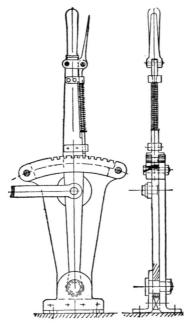

are in use, (1) the older lever and quadrant, Fig. 277, and (2) the screw-reversing device, Fig. 278, which, although slower, requiring about twenty turns of a wheel or handle, is more powerful. The latter characteristic does not always count in model practice, but the screw gear is often found to be simpler to construct as a model. The lever, with its catch handle and notched quadrant, involves rather delicate and precise work if it is to look reasonably true-to-scale.

Manifolds

To save drilling a larger number of holes in the boiler a three- or four-way steam manifold or branch is often fitted to the top of the boiler just behind the cab weatherboard. To this is connected the

Fig. 277.—Cab reversing lever and quadrant.

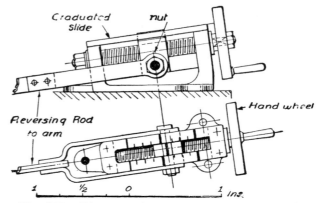

Fig. 278.—Diagram of screw reversing gear in cab

steam gauge, injectors, blower and the steam vacuum-brake fittings, etc. (Fig. 305).

Check Valves (Non-Return or "Clack")

The feed water supply delivered by a pump or injector to the boiler has to be forced against the boiler pressure and held. Thus, in order to prevent the water being forced back again, a check or clack valve is fitted. Any counter-flow of the feed water is held by this valve which automatically closes against the boiler pressure but

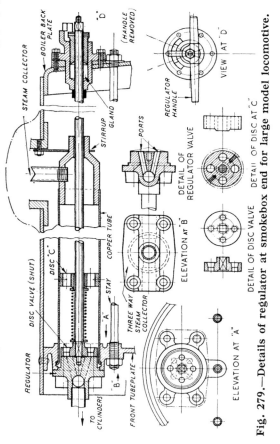

Fig. 279.—Details of regulator at smokebox end for large model locomotive.

opens against injector or pump pressure. The delivery pressure must be in excess of boiler pressure. Standard proprietary check valves are normally obtainable for the larger working models. Fig. 283 shows the assembly of a check valve on the back plate of a boiler.

In fitting check valves to the back of the boiler, it is always advisable to arrange an internal pipe leading to a position half-way along the boiler barrel and below the water level. Where these fittings are screwed into the backplate and not fitted

[243]

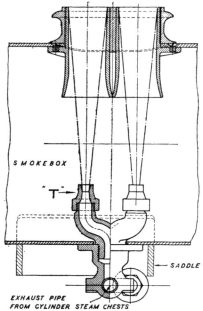

SMOKEBOX

"T"

SADDLE

EXHAUST PIPE
FROM CYLINDER STEAM CHESTS

Fig. 280.—Design for double chimney and blast manifold for large model. (Note: the diameter of each blast nozzle at the throat "T" is approximately 0·7 the diameter of a nozzle fitted to a standard (single) blast pipe. See table XIII.)

by flanged connections the internal pipe may be screwed into the valve, and just before fitting unscrewed the same number of turns (or one more) than the check valve requires to screw it home. Of course, the internal pipe, although not absolutely steam-tight where it joins the valve body, will ensure that most of the water will be carried clear of the firebox plates.

A similar scheme may be used in collecting steam for injectors and blowers by internal pipes from the dome.

In large models the check valve should be provided with an auxiliary screw-down stop valve of the full bore of the pipe.

Pipe Fittings

Two types of blow-off cocks are illustrated in Fig. 284.

A method of attaching small fittings which, like pressure gauges, do not require a large flow of steam or water through them is shown in Fig. 285. The pipe is silver-soldered to a small collar, and this collar is attached by a screw which has been grooved and filed to an almost triangular section below the groove. The steam passes the flats into the groove and so to the pipe connection. Jointing washers are required on both faces of the collar, and B.A. screws are recommended in preference to the Whitworth form for the fixing of the collar. Iron or steel screws should never be used in attaching fittings to copper boilers, and where brass is used it should always be of a good quality.

[244]

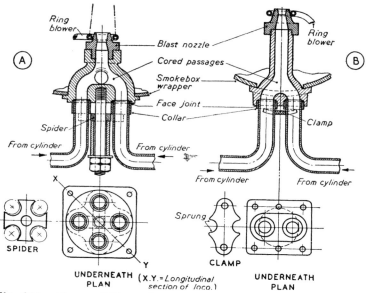

Fig. 281.—Types of blast pipe manifolds. (A) four-way manifold
for two outside piston-valve cylinders and (B) two-way manifold
for two slide-valve cylinders (outside arrangement). Three-way
manifolds are arranged in a similar manner.

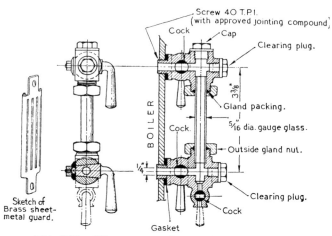

Fig. 282.—Water gauge for model locomotive

[245]

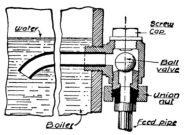

Fig. 283.—Arrangement of check (non-return) valve on back plate of boiler for feed water supply.

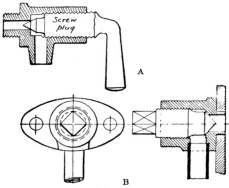

Fig. 284.—(a). Simple screw-down blow-off cock. (b). Detail of drain cock.

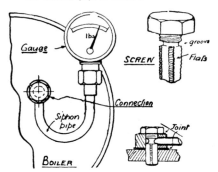

Fig. 285.—Method of fitting pressure gauge for small model

Fire-Doors

Fire-doors of the flap type hinged at the top, have the drawback that they make it difficult to view the fire, and therefore the author uses the flap-down style in their place in cases where such a scheme permits. The sliding type of fire-door is worthy of consideration; two parts, each sliding the opposite way, are generally fitted, the doors being connected by links to a single hand lever.

Smokebox Arrangements

The smokebox of a model locomotive houses numerous fittings, such as the exhaust and steam pipes, blower, and often, in the case of a loco-type boiler,[1] the superheater headers. Space must also be provided for the inside extension of the chimney and petticoat pipe

[1] With a water-tube spirit-fired boiler the super-heater is always carried back through the flames of the lamp.

(Photo: "The Model Engineer")

Fig. 286.—Cab interior of Mr. J. I. Austin-Walton's 0–6–0 tank locomotive (L.M.S.R. No. 11270).

so that even in a large passenger-carrying model there is seldom any great amount of wasted space in the biggest smokebox. The various fittings in a solid fuel model should be arranged in such a manner that the cleaning of the flue tubes is not hindered.

It is quite a safe procedure to allow as much flexibility as possible in the steam pipes in the smokebox, and, in addition, it is highly desirable that the superheater pipes or units should be removable in case of their failure.

To do this it may be policy to attach the front of the smokebox in such a way that it can be removed bodily for the purpose of repairs to the steam pipes, and it is therefore the author's practice to use a cast smokebox front with turned flanges fitting into the end of a cylindrical smokebox.

The arrangement of smokebox superheater shown in Figs. 320 and 320a, although convenient for assembly in the space

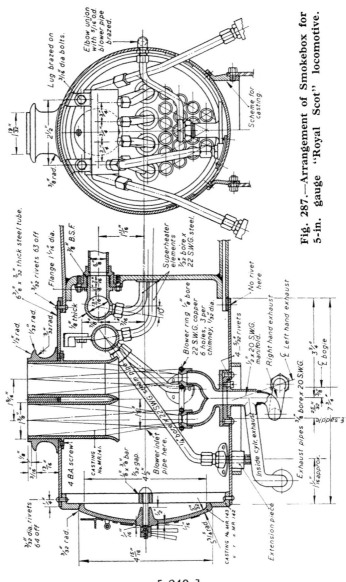

Fig. 287.—Arrangement of Smokebox for 5-in. gauge "Royal Scot" locomotive.

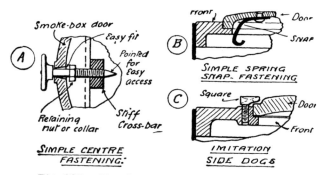

Fig. 288.—Simple smokebox door fastenings.

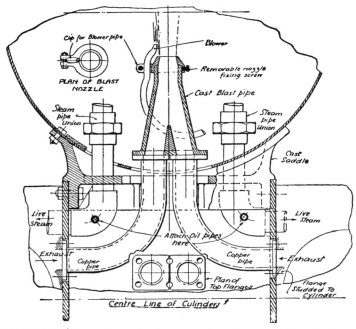

Fig. 289.—Arrangement of steam pipes to outside cylinders and blast manifold. (See Fig. 287.)

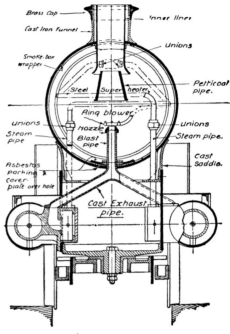

Fig. 290.—Arrangement of Y type exhaust manifold.

available, is not by any means as efficient as the flue-tube type which is in direct contact with the incandescent gases from the firebox. Any arrangement of pipes in the smokebox must be kept clear of the exhaust blast (See Fig. 59, p. 59.)

Where the flue-tube superheater is employed a steel superheater tube is essential with a protective cap at the bend inside the

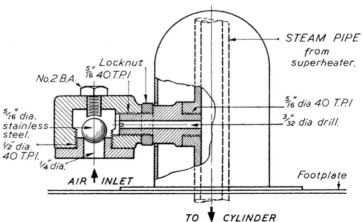

Fig. 291.—"Snifting" or anti-vacuum (self-acting) valve connected direct to steam pipe. The action of the valve is automatic when regulator is shut off.

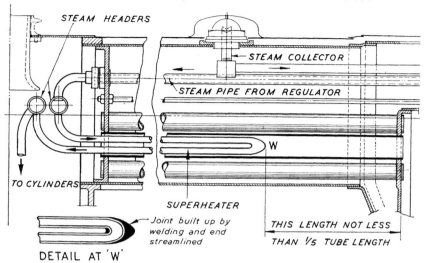

STEAM HEADERS

STEAM COLLECTOR

STEAM PIPE FROM REGULATOR

W

TO CYLINDERS

SUPERHEATER

Joint built up by
welding and end
streamlined

THIS LENGTH NOT LESS
THAN ⅕ TUBE LENGTH

DETAIL AT 'W'

Fig. 292.—Arrangement of spearhead-type superheater for small
model.

flue (Fig. 292). As the temperature of the steam may be
very high the use of iron cylinders and mechanical lubrication
is advisable if not essential to continued success.

It is very important that the smokeboxes of solid fuel boilers
should be absolutely airtight, because they have to sustain a
reduced pressure created by the blast. Holes in the bottom at
the steam pipe entrances may be plugged up with wet asbestos
yarn. With water-tube boilers using a plain spirit or oil burner
the blast need not be so fierce or the smokebox quite so airtight.

In a small model the smokebox door itself does not provide
sufficient room for getting at the pipes and steam connections,
therefore the complete front may be made readily removable.
All large models, more particularly those using solid fuel,
should have hinged doors which fit closely into a recess formed
in the front ring. In modern locomotive practice the central
bolt fastening is often omitted, and buttons or dogs secured by
bolts are fitted round the edge of the door to ensure that the
latter takes an even bearing. The arrangements of the smokebox of a large model are shown by Figs. 287 and 289.

Where the ordinary inside crossbar is employed it should

[251]

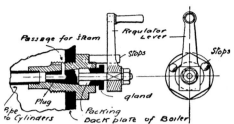

**Fig. 293.—A small model regulator fitted
into the back plate of a small boiler.**

be borne in mind that it acts as a beam loaded in the centre. The bar should therefore be arranged to lie with the wide face horizontal, with its greatest width at the centre, and should also be readily removable. The locking handles or wheel

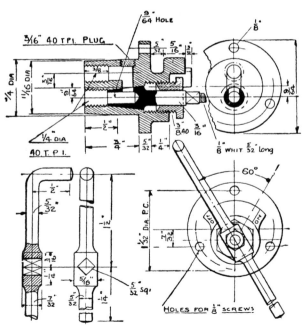

**Fig. 294.—Plug-cock type of regulator with screwed
connections for steam pipes.**

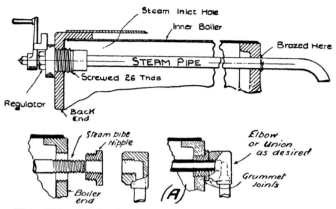

Fig. 295.—Method of assembling steam pipes and connections in smokebox.

nuts should be in duplicate. As a rule, the inside handle is squared for the bolt, but free to move up and down. This only controls the position of the latch head of T, the screwed outside handle or wheel being the tightening device. Simpler constructions are illustrated in Fig. 288. Smoke boxes should be treated with a heat-resisting black paint, and may be lagged inside with a sheet-iron casing.

Snifting Valves

In order to prevent the flue gases overheating the steam pipes and superheater when the regulator is shut, anti-vacuum

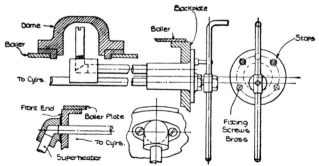

Fig. 296.—Assembly of regulator for a small model locomotive.

[253]

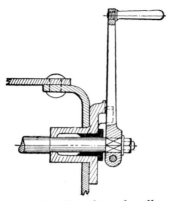

Fig. 297.—Regulator handle and gland fitting for Stroudley regulator.

Fig. 298. — Dome removed to show working model Stroudley regulator.

or snifting valves should be fitted to locomotives. When the regulator is closed, the steam remaining in the feed pipes condenses and a partial vacuum is created. Atmospheric pressure immediately opens the snifting valve and air is admitted to cool the superheater and pipes. Fig. 291 illustrates the type of anti-vacuum valve fitted to a 1½-in. scale locomotive designed by the author.

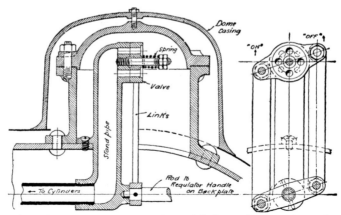

Fig. 299.—Arrangement of model Stroudly regulator for large model.

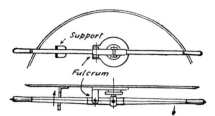

Fig. 300.—Old type of "push and pull" regulator handle.

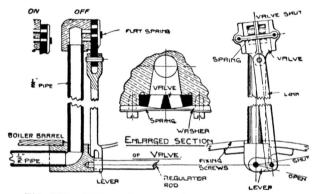

Fig. 301.—Slide valve type of regulator in dome.

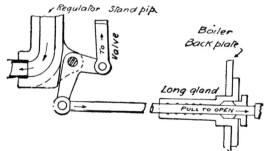

Fig. 302.—Push and pull mechanism for small model.

[255]

Blast Pipes

These are generally of circular section, but other shapes could be employed by way of experiment viz. annular, twin-circular etc. Information bearing on the importance and position of this very vital part has already been included in Chapter IV. The use of a removable or renewable cap is always to be recommended, while the concentricity of the jet in respect to the chimney is a point on which the utmost care should be exercised. The provision of an adjustment to the orifice in larger engines is worthy of experiment.

TABLE XIII
SINGLE BLAST PIPE ORIFICES

Bore of Cylinder inches	Diameter of Orifice—inches		
	2 Cylinders	3 Cylinders	4 Cylinders
$\frac{1}{2}$	$\frac{3}{32}$ — $\frac{7}{64}$	—	—
$\frac{5}{8}$	$\frac{7}{64}$ — $\frac{1}{8}$	—	—
$\frac{3}{4}$	$\frac{9}{64}$ — $\frac{5}{32}$	$\frac{11}{64}$ — $\frac{3}{16}$	—
1	$\frac{11}{64}$	$\frac{3}{16}$	$\frac{1}{4}$
$1\frac{1}{4}$	$\frac{7}{32}$	$\frac{17}{64}$	$\frac{5}{16}$
$1\frac{1}{2}$	$\frac{1}{4}$	$\frac{5}{16}$	$\frac{11}{32}$
$1\frac{3}{4}$	$\frac{9}{32}$	$\frac{11}{32}$	$\frac{13}{32}$
2	$\frac{11}{32}$	$\frac{27}{64}$	$\frac{1}{2}$
$2\frac{1}{2}$	$\frac{27}{64}$	$\frac{33}{64}$	$\frac{19}{32}$
3	$\frac{21}{32}$	$\frac{31}{32}$	$\frac{3}{4}$
4	$\frac{25}{32}$	$\frac{31}{32}$	$1\frac{1}{16}$
5	$1\frac{1}{8}$	$1\frac{3}{8}$	—
$5\frac{1}{4}$	$1\frac{1}{4}$	$1\frac{1}{2}$	

(E. A. Steel)

The exhaust steam from the cylinders should be led as directly as possible to the blast pipe orifice. Great changes in the cross-sectional area of the pipes, as well as any baffling of the flow of the steam, should be avoided. Fig. 289 shows an arrangement of exhaust steam pipe fitted to one of the author's 15 in. gauge designs.

Regulators

The main steam stop valve of a locomotive, as its name "regulator" implies, regulates at the driver's will the flow of

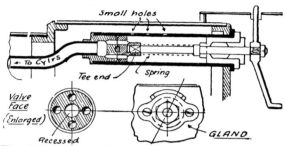

Fig. 303.—Disc valve regulator for small model.

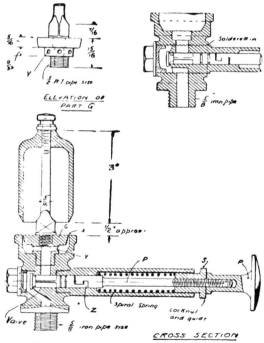

Fig. 304.—Details of steam whistle.

steam to the cylinders, the lever operating the steam valve being placed in a convenient position in the cab.

Where the engine is a simple one, and a realistic arrangement of fittings in the cab is relatively unimportant, a plain plug-cock fixed outside the back plate of the boiler may be fitted. An alternative arrangement is to use a small screw-down valve in the main feed pipe.

Among the regulators made for small gauge models the plug-cock type illustrated in Fig. 293 is perhaps the best known. The regulator body is screwed with a fine thread into a tapped hole in the cast back plate of the boiler. Steam is admitted through a small hole on the top of the regulator. The only drawback to the arrangement is that water may be carried over with the steam. The arrangement (Fig. 295) shows the method of assembling the steam pipe and regulator. Here the steam pipe is screwed with a fine thread for a nipple having an outer thread of larger diameter but with the same pitch. The nipple can be screwed on the pipe and into the boiler end at the same time, and the joint made secure by a back nut or by the elbow or union employed to connect the superheater pipe.

The plug-cock regulator (Figs. 294 and 296) is an improvement on the one just described in that the body provides for the connection of a second collecting pipe from the dome. The regulator takes a little more room on the boiler back plate, but is much to be preferred in spite of this. The illustration also shows a method of connecting the superheater steam pipe at the smokebox end. The small gunmetal block under the dome serves as a support and an elbow to the collecting pipe for screwing in the short vertical pipe from the highest point in the boiler.

A type of regulator used on domed engines in this country comprises a stand-pipe in the dome with a sliding or rotating valve at its head. The valve is connected by links and levers to a long regulator rod which passes through a stuffing box on the back plate of the firebox to the driver's regulator handle.

The valve in the dome is usually duplex, one part being a pilot to the other. This scheme is not necessary in a model, as the valves are small relative to the power available to move them. The rotating or "Stroudley" type of regulator is illustrated in Figs. 297, 298 and 299, and is a very satisfactory arrangement so long as the valve is accurately made. The centre portion of

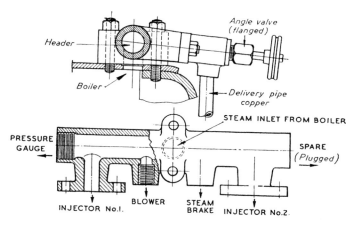

PLAN OF MANIFOLD HEADER

Fig. 305.—Cast manifold as fitted to back of boiler for auxiliary steam feeds to injectors, blower, pressure gauges and steam brake supply etc.

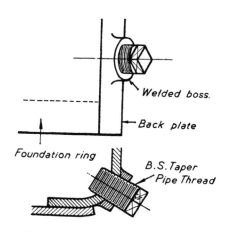

Fig. 306.—Boiler wash-out plug.

both valve and port face *must be recessed*. The only complaints in large model practice investigated by the author showed that the leakage was caused through the mechanics failing to observe this important point. Two links are employed to connect the valve to the spindle and handle. This is an excellent feature, as the valve is always "pulled" open or shut.

In some cases a push-and-pull lever is employed in the cab (Fig. 300). This arrangement was standard at one time on the G.N.R. Singles (P. Stirling), and was used in conjunction with domeless boilers, a slide valve regulator in the smokebox at the end of a long perforated collecting box being used.

The slide valve type of regulator, arranged in a built-up form for a large model, is illustrated in Fig. 301. The stand-pipe is made from tube, and is screwed into a solid head and elbow. The valve should be of a different grade of material from the seating and may have two sets of ports as shown. The regulator rod has a single lever set to operate the valve at an angle, the connecting link being stiff enough to act as a push rod against the friction on the valve created by the pressure of steam on its surface. All parts should be of cast iron, brass or gunmetal. The flat spring and screws must be of non-ferrous material to resist corrosion. Stainless steel fittings can also be employed.

The type of regulator shown in Fig. 301 may be operated by a pull-out regulator rod and lever by altering the scheme of levers at the heel of the stand-pipe, as illustrated in Fig. 302. As the surface of the regulator rod is more likely to score in grooves at the gland, a long gland and stuffing box is advisable with this style of lever to prevent any annoying leakage of steam. The packing must also be quite tight, otherwise the pressure of steam acting on the rod will tend to open the regulator.

A horizontal slide-valve regulator placed in the smokebox under a dome or in a raised firebox is sometimes employed. In whatever way it is arranged, the subsequent removal of the valve and repair of the port face should be considered.

A design for a rotating valve regulator suitable for a dome-less raised-firebox boiler (G.W.R. type) is illustrated in Fig. 303. The regulator valve is situated at the front of the tube, as far away from the back plate as possible, and is operated by a T-headed spindle working through a gland, the valve

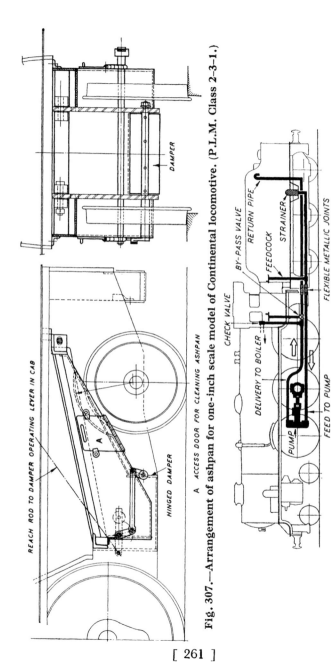

A ACCESS DOOR FOR CLEANING ASHPAN

Fig. 307.—Arrangement of ashpan for one-inch scale model of Continental locomotive. (P.L.M. Class 2–3–1.)

Fig. 308.—Diagram showing feed-water supply from tender to boiler. When the axle-driven pump is not required the by-pass valve is kept open to allow free circulation of water externally. The system can be employed in conjunction with an injector system.

being maintained in place by a bronze spiral spring. The valve and its facing must be both recessed centrally and chamfered at the edges, so that it bears only over the shaded portion indicated on the enlarged view of its surface. The space between the ports must be greater than the diameter of the holes.

Whistles

To preserve the scale effect from an external point of view a whistle may be partly concealed in the cab. It may be placed so that only the top bell protrudes through the cab roof. If connected to a part of the boiler below the highest level it should be supplied by an internal, not an external, steam pipe to prevent radiation condensing the steam. Plug-cocks are not entirely satisfactory. A good whistle designed for a $1\frac{1}{2}$-in. scale locomotive, is illustrated in Fig. 304. This has a push valve worked by a spring-loaded plunger loosely attached at z. The additional sectional view shows an alternative method of making the valve seat and guide.

Top Water Feed

For a large-scale model locomotive arrangements can be made for water to be pumped or injected into the top of the boiler and through suitable check valves placed in a position well forward from the firebox as in real practice. In full-size practice, the feed water is allowed to spray over a series of trays mounted in the steam space until it reaches the surface of the boiler water at a temperature approximating to that of steam. Some arrangement that will achieve the same result is required, always taking into account the limitations of space and accessibility.

CHAPTER XIV

GENERAL FITMENTS, TENDERS AND DRAWGEAR

THE general fittings and attachments that go to make the characteristic features of a prototype should be copied "true-to-scale" as closely as the design of a *working* model will permit. External features such as the sheet metal work generally, cabs, saddles, handrails, steps and buffers etc., should exhibit a robustness of design in keeping with the qualities expected of locomotives as a machine for doing useful work.

Superstructures

Plates from $\frac{3}{16}$ in. to $\frac{1}{4}$ in. thick are employed in standard gauge locomotives. They are bolted or welded to steel angles or tee sections. While sheet materials for all the superstructures of a model are used, castings may also be used to some advantage. Where four or more wheel splashers are required and they are identical, a metal pattern can be fabricated and castings made from it. Aluminium alloy castings can be specified for various small fitments.

In a 1-in. scale model the ruling thickness would be No. 16 I.S.G. ($\frac{1}{16}$ in.) to No. 14 I.S.G. Angle brass as small as $\frac{1}{4}$ in. $\times \frac{1}{4}$ in. can be specified, but where a water container is used the combination of steel sheets (other than tinned plate) and angle brass should be avoided. Brass throughout or a copper inner tank is to be preferred, the inside of the body of the superstructure masking the inner tank, and being thoroughly painted before the tank is fitted into place.

Along the edges of the footplating of a locomotive stiffening angles are fitted and in almost all cases the footplating overlaps this edging. Steel or brass angle may be used, although in a smaller model the use of solid brass rod of rectangular section is the best practice, especially where the footplates have curves introduced into them. Figs. 309 and 310 show various methods of construction at the ends of such stiffeners, and Fig. 311 how

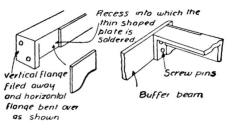

Fig. 309.—Details of edgings for footplates.

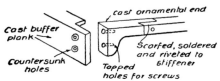

Fig. 310.—Details of edging for attachment to front buffer plank.

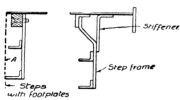

Fig. 311.—Simple footsteps for small models. Front of step must not extend beyond the point marked "A". For No. 1 gauge steps may be cast in one piece.

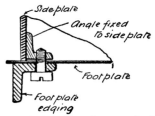

Fig. 312.—Simple method of fixing superstructure to chassis.

steps are usually fitted to the footplates. Steps may be cast in one piece.

Cabs

In building splashers, tanks and cabs of small models short lengths of angle or strip for fixing two plates at right angles may be utilized, the first operation being to solder and screw or pin the angle or square strip to one plate slightly short of the edge and then attach to the other plate by screws after the manner indicated in the section of a dummy side tank (Fig. 312). The plates may be soldered along the whole joint afterwards if a permanent fixing is desirable. If any accident should subject the upper works of the engine to fire, or if further soldering is to be done to the work, it will not fall to pieces in the way it would if no positive fixing were employed other than the solder.

For edging cabs and tender sides half-round brass wire from $\frac{1}{16}$-in. diameter can be used,

Fig. 313.—Beading for cabs, tanks and coal rails.

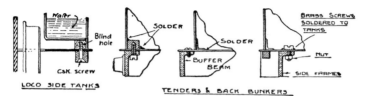

Fig. 314.—Methods of fixing tanks.

Fig. 315a.—Model of eight-wheeled diamond bogie tender.

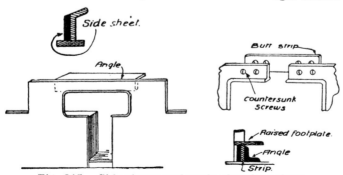

Fig. 315.—Side sheets and roofs of tank engines.

[265]

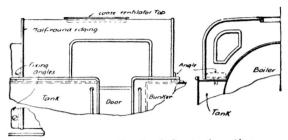

Fig. 316.—Details of cab for tank engine.

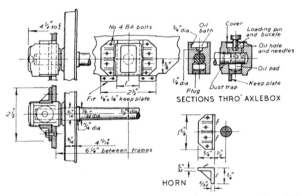

Fig. 317.—Details of 5-in. gauge tender horns and axlebox.

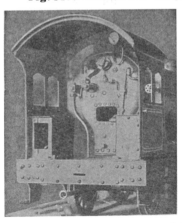

Fig. 318.—Details of cab for
1-in. scale model of North
Eastern Railway locomotive.

while from $\frac{3}{32}$-in. diameter upwards a section of wire (see Fig. 313), known in the silversmith trade as "catch wire," is extremely useful.

Repairs to both engines and tenders will be greatly facilitated if splashers, cabs, tanks, etc., are made entirely separate from boilers and underframes, and also secured in such a manner that the component parts may be readily removed. In a tank engine having side and bunker tanks, the arrangement of fixing down to footplates illustrated at A Fig. 314 may be adopted. Where wheels interfere with side tanks the tanks can be of the full width and recessed locally or may be of narrow width throughout their whole length as shown. The additional views, B, of this illustration show methods of fixing-down tender tanks.

Connecting side tanks to bunkers where the side plates are flush is a feature which needs attention from the point of view of construction and also taking the components apart for repairs. The side sheets may be cut over and below the doorway and fishplate strips arranged to connect the two sheets. Where the bunker and side tanks can be in one piece and lifted off clear of the boiler the raised footboard in the cab may allow a continuous side sheet to be used, the narrow strips connecting top and bottom being reinforced by short lengths of brass rod or angle.

There are several designs where it is possible to make the cab as a separate structure. An example of this is illustrated in Fig. 316. In this way the connecting screws with their unsightly slots do not come on the painted and lined faces of the tanks and bunkers, but on the relatively unimportant top surfaces. The L.N.W.R. type of cab allows a similar construction in the case of tender engines owing to the design having two or three component parts, i.e. the lower side sheets on each side and the covering portion.

The glazing for the front spectacles of cabs and, where applicable, side windows, is of thin glass. The fixings should be of the simplest and the glass held loosely otherwise heat from the firebox will crack the window if secured too rigidly.

Saddles for Smokeboxes

The saddle is an important feature of a locomotive for it not only supports the smokebox but acts as a main stretcher

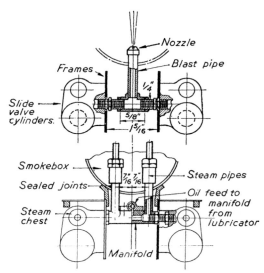

Fig. 319.—Steam manifold and exhaust arrangements for No. 1 gauge model.

for the frames and houses the various steam and exhaust pipe manifolds. It can either be a casting or made up from steel stock bar or angles welded or riveted together according to the size of engine. Various types of saddles are shown by Figs. 320 and 321.

For modern three-cylinder locomotives it is sometimes necessary to cut away a portion of the saddle to clear the inside cylinder. In the case of a cast saddle, the pattern can of course be modified accordingly. The left- and right-hand sides of the saddle parallel to centre-line of the engine must be carefully machined to between-frames dimension. Provision should also be made for the saddle to seat on top of the frames. This relieves the bolts of shear due to the weight of the smokebox, boiler and other fittings.

Handrails, Knobs, etc.

Many excellent models are often spoiled by disproportionate handrails and knobs. In full-size practice $1\frac{1}{8}$-in. or $1\frac{1}{4}$-in. tube is

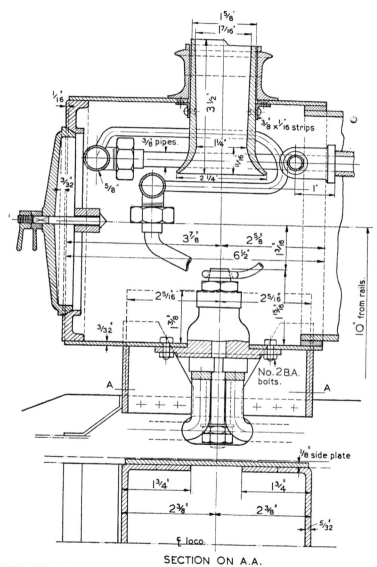

SECTION ON A.A.

Fig. 320.—Arrangement of smokebox for Greenly 5-in. gauge free-lance model 4–6–4 tank locomotive.

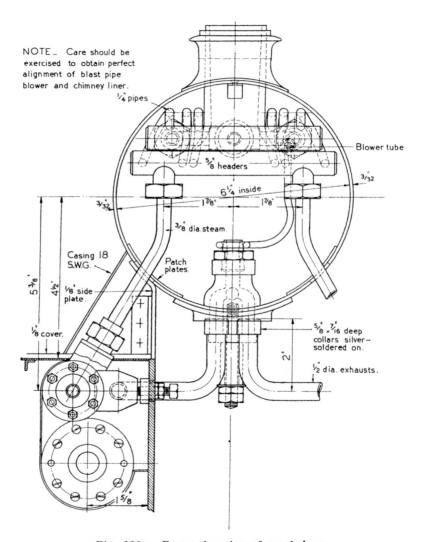

NOTE_ Care should be exercised to obtain perfect alignment of blast pipe blower and chimney liner.

$\frac{1}{4}''$ pipes

Blower tube

$\frac{5}{8}''$ headers

$6\frac{1}{4}''$ inside

$3/_{32}$

$1\frac{7}{8}''$ $1\frac{7}{8}''$

$3/_{32}$

$\frac{3}{8}''$ dia. steam

Casing 18 S.W.G.

Patch plates.

$\frac{1}{8}''$ side plate.

$\frac{1}{8}''$ cover.

$5\frac{3}{8}''$

$4\frac{1}{2}''$

$\frac{5}{8}'' \times \frac{7}{16}''$ deep collars silver—soldered on.

2''

$\frac{1}{2}''$ dia. exhausts.

$1\frac{5}{8}''$

Fig. 320a.—Front elevation of smokebox.

[270]

employed, but in a small model the handrail may be a little thicker than a strict scale equivalent would suggest. For a 1-in. scale engine use No. 12 s.w.g. steel rod, for ¾-in. scale No. 15, and for smaller models No. 18 or No. 20 gauge.

In a lagged boiler handrails are fitted to the cleading, which is locally strengthened by a strip of thicker metal inside; otherwise they must be screwed into the boiler and made steamtight. Steel knobs should never be put into the shell of a copper boiler. Non-ferrous fittings should always be employed in such cases.

Tenders

The function of a locomotive tender is to carry the fuel and water required by the engine, and, as its name implies, it is quite a separate vehicle, often weighing when loaded nearly two-thirds that of the engine itself.

The standard British tender is usually a six-wheeled carriage, the total wheel base, which is rigid, varying from 12 ft. to 16 ft. Where the railway is provided with water troughs and pick-up

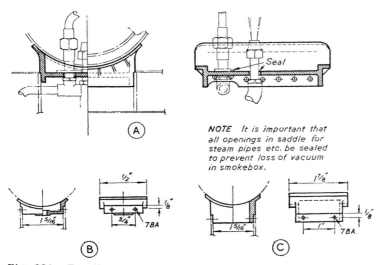

NOTE It is important that all openings in saddle for steam pipes etc. be sealed to prevent loss of vacuum in smokebox.

Fig. 321.—Details of saddles. (A) Large models (B and C) No. 1 gauge models.

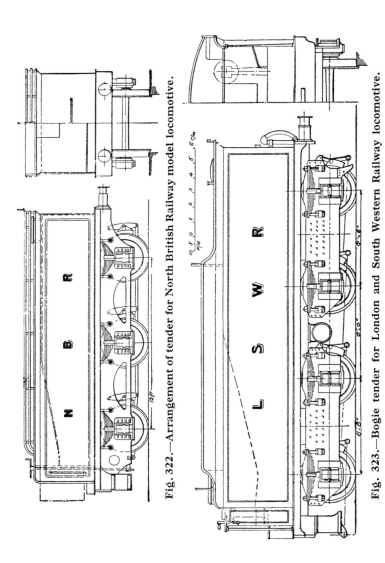

Fig. 322.—Arrangement of tender for North British Railway model locomotive.

Fig. 323.—Bogie tender for London and South Western Railway locomotive.

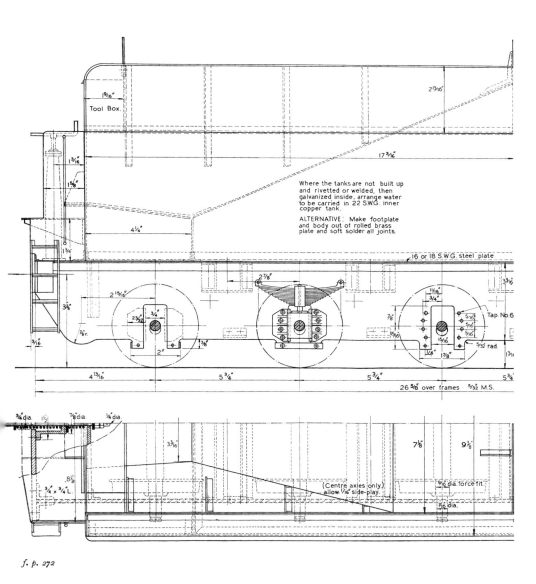

Where the tanks are not built up
and rivetted or welded, then
galvanized inside. arrange water
to be carried in 22 S.W.G. inner
copper tank.

ALTERNATIVE : Make footplate
and body out of rolled brass
plate and soft solder all joints.

Tool Box.

16 or 18 S.W.G. steel plate

Tap. No.6

(Centre axles only.)
allow 1/16" side-play.

26 5/8 over frames

f. p. 272

Fig. 324A - Tender for 5 in. gauge model of the British "Austerity"

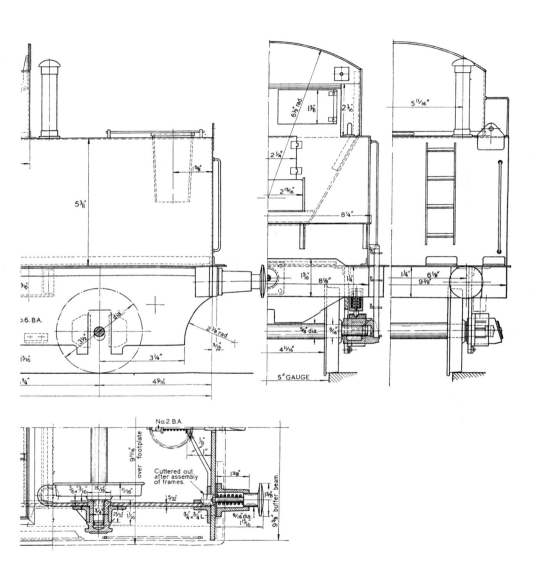

Fig. 324B - Tender for 5 in. gauge model of the British "Austerity"

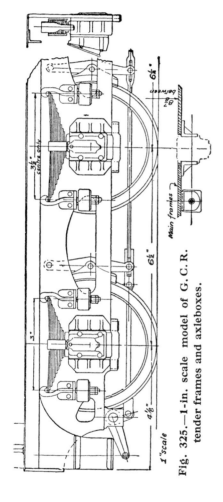

Fig. 325.—1-in. scale model of G.C.R. tender frames and axleboxes.

Fig. 326.—15-in. gauge eight-wheeled bogie tender.

tenders the capacity averages 3,500 to 5,000 gallons and four to nine tons of coal. The eight-wheeled (twin bogie) tender is also standard practice in this country (S.R.). There is also the type equipped with a corridor communicating with the train. Whilst the general outline of the tender, together with its water pick-up apparatus, can be made true-to-scale, the provision of the actual corridor in a working model serves no useful purpose and can be omitted.

All modern tenders have outside frames. The old Brighton six-wheelers and Drummond's L.S.W.R. bogie tenders have wheels with inside axleboxes and therefore are easy to model. The springs in modern engines are almost universally on top of the axleboxes and below the footplate level. Water pick-up apparatus can be fitted in order to complete the model, and to demonstrate its operation, but is unlikely to be used in practice.

The axlebox frames of earlier types were separate units attached to the main frames, as in the case of a wagon or carriage. This is not a bad idea for a small model, as only one pattern for these frames and the dummy springs (if used) need be made, six being cast off it. A double-bogie tender requires pivots for the trucks only; no side play being necessary. The turning movement on a curve is very small indeed.

(Photo: Courtesy of J. Austin Walton, Esq.)

Fig. 327.—5-in. gauge model of L.M.S.R. Tender built by Mr. J. Austin Walton.

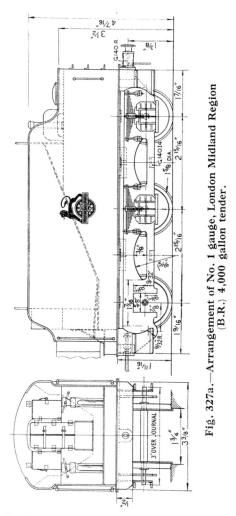

Fig. 327a.—Arrangement of No. 1 gauge, London Midland Region (B.R.) 4,000 gallon tender.

One of the largest types of American locomotives of the N.Y.C.R., the 4-8-4 "Niagara" class, has a fourteen-wheel tender comprising ten wheels on a fixed base and a leading four-wheel bogie.

The arrangement of bunkers or tanks for spirit or oil fired

[275]

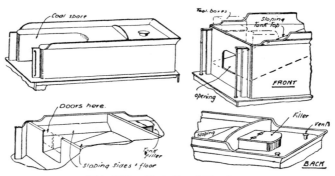

Fig. 328.—Details of Tenders.

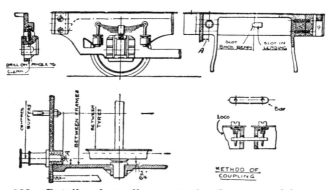

Fig. 329.—Details of small cast tender frames, axleboxes, etc.

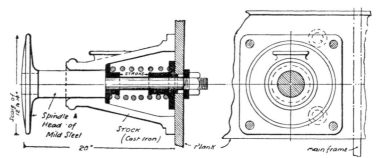

Fig. 330.—Details of buffer for large model. (Conical stock.)

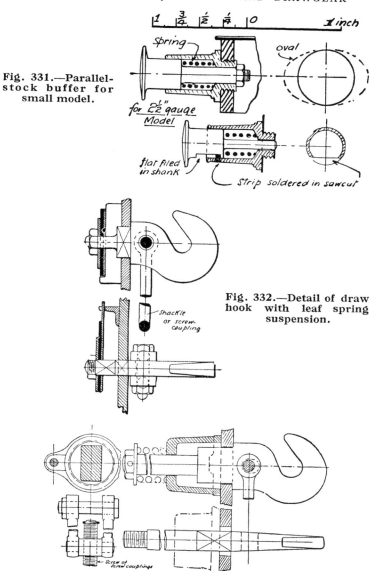

Fig. 331.—Parallel-stock buffer for small model.

Fig. 332.—Detail of draw hook with leaf spring suspension.

Fig. 333.—Another form of spring tension drawhook.

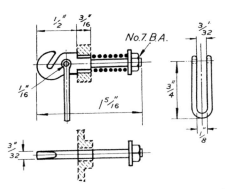

Fig. 334.—Detail of No. 1 gauge drawhook.

engines requires consideration. Sometimes the maker of the model will choose to mask the presence of spirit or oil tanks; others will not mind the liquid fuel containers being seen. This, of course, affects the internal design of the tender body. Fig. 328 shows three forms of bunkers and tanks.

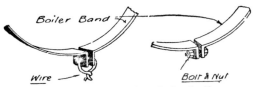

Fig. 335.—Lagging bands for boilers.

Tender side frames may, if several engines of small gauge are required, be cast in soft iron or brass in one piece complete with dummy springs, axlebox guides, etc. Where the wheels are sprung the horn-stays should be cast solid with the frames

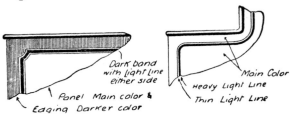

Fig. 336.—Methods of lining.

at the bottom of the axlebox guides A spiral spring can then be concealed in the buckle without disturbing the horn-stay. Another point needing special attention is the relative position of the buffers, and the joint of the main frames and buffer planks indicated at A in Fig. 329. Here a cast plank is used into which the buffers screw, sufficiently large bosses being arranged at the back of the plank for this purpose and for providing a fixing for the screws attaching the side frames. A simple method of arranging the guard irons and coupling the locomotive is also illustrated. The former are cast in brass solid with the plank. They may be bent to the required shape.

In the case of plate frames dummy springs are cast separately and slung in the usual manner as if they were real laminated springs, acting spiral springs in the buckle or on the spring hangers being employed.

For $\frac{3}{4}$-in. scale and over the model maker may prefer the greater realism of working laminated leaf springs, provided they can be adjusted to give the desired amount of deflection. One method of doing this is to reduce the effective cross section of every other leaf by slotting. Another method is to substitute packing plates between the leaves; the number of laminations being reduced accordingly.

Buffers

There are two patterns in general use, one with the conical and the other with the parallel stock. The heads are sometimes oval, when keys and keyways in the stalk of the buffer or other means must be provided to prevent them turning, devices for this purpose not always being entirely successful in real practice. The conical buffer illustrated in Fig. 330 represents one made for a large model, the collars on the spindle being made sufficiently long to protect the spring from damage under full load. Springs may be duplicated, one being placed inside the other, and one being much stronger and shorter, so that it only comes into action during the last part of the stroke. A pair of spring buffers should just close when loaded to a weight equal to one-fourth that of the engine. This is a rough guide to the required strength of the springs. A simple arrangement of spring buffers (parallel type) is illustrated in Fig. 331, a method of preventing the heads turning (where they are of oval shape)

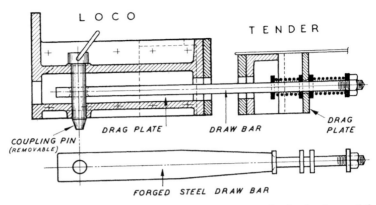

Fig. 337.—Method of coupling tender to locomotive for large model.

being indicated in the lower part of the sketch. Buffer heads should be made of steel in small models, and may be separate from the spindle, as shown in Fig. 330, if a secure fastening of the heads on to the spindle is devised.

Fig. 338.—Assembly of 2½-in. gauge chassis, motion and boiler for tank locomotive (ten-coupled).

Drawhooks

These should be made of steel, and in small models are often screwed or riveted and soldered into the buffer planks. The illustrations (Figs. 332, 333 and 334) show three methods of providing spring suspension.

In such cases the shank of the hook, where it passes through the plank, must be squared to prevent the rotation of the hook in service. In engines having long overhanging frames at the leading or trailing ends, it is necessary to allow a wide slot in the buffer plank and to extend the shank back some distance to a suitable fixing so that the hook can swing from side to side.

Special forms of hooks and shackles are necessary in small-gauge models operating on excessively sharp curves. In these it is usual to arrange an inverted T- slot in the hook and a rigid shackle. In this way the train can be pushed through the couplings and "buffer-locking" eliminated. A pivoted draw-hook with ample lateral play is essential to this device.

Lagging

The lagging of a model boiler with asbestos yarn or millboard flannel soaked in alum, the whole being covered with a cleading of sheet metal (tin-plate, or rolled-brass sheet), is not always a satisfactory or interesting job to the amateur. For small models the use of lagging cuts down the internal dimensions of the boiler an appreciable amount, and if a reasonably smooth, clean job is made of the boiler itself there is no need to use lagging. The saving in heat loss is likely to be less that 10%, while the reduction in heating surface and boiler may prove to be a more serious item. Thin sheet metal cleading can be wrapped round the boiler and secured, leaving a small air gap between. This will be found to give quite a good degree of heat insulation to the boiler.

The cleading in real engines is laid on in several sheets, and the circular joints are covered by bands of thin metal. The width of the bands employed in actual practice varies from $1\frac{3}{4}$ in. to $2\frac{1}{2}$ in. For models strip brass, upwards of $\frac{1}{32}$ in. thick, in various widths, can be used. Fig. 335 shows two methods of joining up the ends at the underside of the barrel.

Water-tube boilers having outer casings in contact with the flame and not at water heat are subject to the rapid

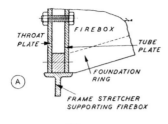

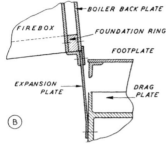

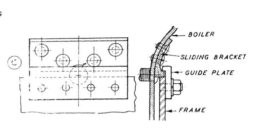

Fig. 339.—Types of expansion
brackets for boilers.

deterioration of the enamel. The only method to overcome the
trouble satisfactorily is to use a double casing—virtually a
lagging of the outer shell—this double casing being packed
with asbestos. An air space may be provided between the two
casings in place of the asbestos.

For a large model (1½-in. scale and upwards) asbestos yarn
or string is the most convenient material to use for the
lagging. It can be wound round and round the barrel and
laid in ropes side by side over the firebox portion.

Two styles of paint lining are shown in Fig. 336.

Fixing Boilers

Boilers are usually firmly fixed to the frames at the smokebox end, but at the back some scheme must be devised to hold
the firebox down to the frames and at the same time permit
movement to allow for thermal expansion. The usual method is
to fit an angle to the firebox side which rests on the top edge
of the frames and to bolt another angle to the latter and
lapping over the boiler angle. The design and location of
expansion brackets supporting the boiler will depend upon
the type of firebox employed. For a boiler with a wide firebox,

three-point suspension can be provided at the base of the foundation ring. The front of the ring is supported on a shoe resting on a main frame stretcher, and the rear can be supported on two brackets fixed to the drag plate (See Fig. 339).

A boiler with a narrow firebox is supported on a pair of expansion brackets fixed to the main frames and, if necessary for strength, to an additional bracket fixed to the drag plate. The longitudinal thermal expansion for the boiler of a $7\frac{1}{4}$ in. gauge "pacific" type locomotive is from $\frac{1}{8}$ to $\frac{3}{16}$ in. according to the temperature of the steam. Provision must also be made for transverse expansion of the firebox in all cases.

Fig. 339a.—Model of G.W.R. Tender.

CHAPTER XV

FIRING AND BOILER-FEEDING DEVICES

Spirit Firing

THE externally-fired engine requires either a plain wick burner or one in which the spirit is vaporised by a regenerative action coupled with the heat obtained from a small wick tube or pilot light. The vaporising burner (Fig. 340) is good where there is natural ventilation of the flame, but does not appear to have been used with any degree of success in a closed firebox with induced draught. Methylated spirit vapour has a very characteristic flame. If the speed of the vapour issuing from a jet rises beyond a very low limit it will not remain ignited—the flame will leave the jet.

The spirit wick tube most often gives trouble in home-made engines through its component parts being made of heavy-gauge copper tubes. The heat is conducted through these pipes to the reservoir, causing the spirit to boil. Care should be taken to select the thinnest tubes; further, the open drip trough so frequently used is the cause of many a "flare up".

Another point to remember in applying a spirit tube to an internally fired engine is that while an induced draught is essential in promoting complete combustion, the furnace should not be so small or the wick tubes so closely arranged that the blast of the engine lifts the flame off the wicks and simply draws unburnt spirit up the chimney. The fuel is not only too expensive to waste in this way, *but the vapour fumes are highly objectionable where the railway is indoors*. It is possible with a small firebox and a sharp draught that less steam will be generated when the engine is running than when it is standing still and the spirit burning under natural draught only or with the help of a small steam blower.

Wicks should not be crowded too close together, and, in any case, the tops of the wick tubes should be as far away as possible (up to 2 in.) from the underside of the water tubes. In connection with the subject of spacing, for any locomotive with a long narrow "grate" the system of oval wicks placed transversely across the firebox, as sketched in Fig.341, may be favourably considered. Here there are four intermediate air spaces of relatively large dimensions, and as

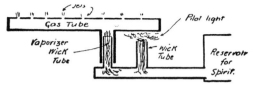

Fig. 340.—Diagram showing arrangement of vaporizing spirit lamp for externally-fired No. 1 gauge boilers.

the draught induces the flame across these air spaces cold air playing on the tubes will be to a certain degree eliminated. Threading strands of wick across the open spaces is often practised for the same reason. Another method of moderating the less desirable effects of a sharp draught on a burner is to drill holes in the top of the wick tubes, more particularly the sides facing the spaces between the tubes. Vaporized spirit emerges from these holes and is ignited by the wicks. A development of these ideas is a burner designed for a wide firebox. The burner is an annular trough, across which wires are stretched for supporting asbestos yarn. Holes are drilled all round the inside of the wick trough, the intention being to provide an incandescent mass in the centre reproducing the effect of a thin coal fire; the large area of the firebox only requiring a very moderate induced draught.

The spirit burner is not of any service in firing a loco-type boiler with tubular flues. The only condition under which any measure of success will be obtained with a flue-tube boiler is where water tubes in the firebox are present and where all the heat-conducting surfaces are of the thinnest material consistent with the strength required. Some of such water tubes should be arranged to promote an end-to-end circulation of the water in the boiler.

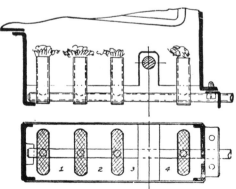

Fig. 341. — Arrangement of spirit burners in firebox of water-tube boiler, No. 0 and No. 1 gauge locomotives.

Wicks should be made up of asbestos yarn. This material conducts the spirit quite well and does not char. In the arrangement shown in Fig. 344 a sump is placed behind the tender buffer beam. Protection from the flame of the burner is provided by the baffle plate w, which also forms a means of fixing the lamp, and a drip plate. When the spirit overflows the flaming fuel tends to run along the supply tubes and ignite the open sump. The plate should prevent this occurring. For engines working on excessively-sharp curves the open-topped tube leading the drops of spirit to the sump may have to be oval instead of round as shown. This is a matter to be considered in designing a lamp for a particular locomotive. The overflow pipe should be extended laterally clear of the wheels, so that an excess of feed may be readily observed.

Where a coiled feed pipe scheme is adopted, as in Fig. 346, the pipe must not be too small otherwise capillary action will be set up. The coil should be wound with a constant fall to allow the fuel to flow freely. Care must be taken to ensure that no air locks are present in the system.

Fig. 342.—Auxiliary blower and boiler for steam raising.

Fig. 343.—Underside of model 0-4-4 locomotive showing spirit burners.

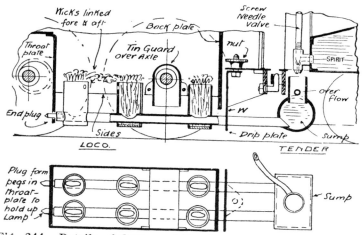

Fig. 344.—Details of firebox of No. 0 gauge spirit-fired engine with drip-feed attachment on tender.

In all wick-siphon feeds the spirit supply may be stopped by withdrawing the wick from the reservoir. Alternatively a cock may be fitted on the supply pipe or means provided for compressing the wick at the top.

The ratio of the weight of steam generated to liquid fuel consumed is approximately 4 to 1.

Solid-fuel Firing

Undoubtedly generating steam from solid fuel is highly satisfactory, and should be adopted. With the spirit and oil burner the fire is not under control, and, what is more important than anything, the range of intensity does not vary

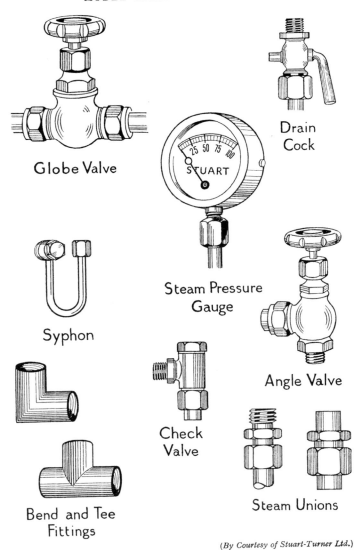

Globe Valve

Drain Cock

Syphon

Steam Pressure Gauge

Angle Valve

Check Valve

Steam Unions

Bend and Tee Fittings

(By Courtesy of Stuart-Turner Ltd.)

Fig. 345.—Examples of steam fittings for model locomotive boilers.

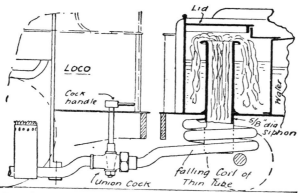

Fig. 346.—Diagram of Wick-siphon feed system for small models.

directly with the load on the engine as expressed by the value
of the blast exhaust steam. If a model locomotive fired by spirit
is forced beyond a given point the flames are deflected so much
by the fierce induced draught that the heat in the furnace is
reduced and the generation of steam falls instead of rises. This
cannot happen, with reasonable attention, to a coal or charcoal
fire. As in a real locomotive, evaporation will increase and
diminish automatically with the demands of the engine.

To regulate a solid-fuel engine—it must not be forgotten
that the skill of a locomotive fireman is as important a factor
as that of the driver—the following means are used:

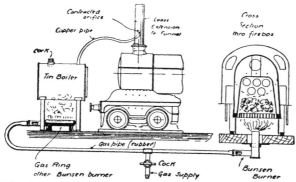

Fig. 347.—Method of raising steam from gas supply.

(a) The supply of fuel and its timing compared with
(b) The supply of feed water and its periodicity.
(c) The regulation of the air above and below the fire.
(d) The use of the steam blower when standing.
(e) The intensity of the exhaust blast, which in a large model is variable at the wish of the driver and varies automatically by the resistance of the load. Sometimes in real practice devices are used to vary the area of the blast nozzle.

Whilst there are limits to the thickness of an incandescent fire if coal alone is used, a charcoal fire may be filled up to the crown of the firebox. Firebox capacity is therefore one of the chief aims in the design of a charcoal-fired engine. A thick fire may be used where coke is employed, but such fuel is not to be recommended in a copper firebox or in a boiler with copper tubes.

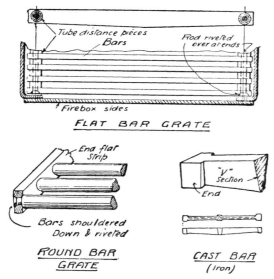

Fig. 348.—Details of types of firebars.

Where a solid-fuel engine of small dimensions is concerned the only difficulties that will present themselves are those due to the absence of a fireman on the engine. If sent away on a continuous run with a heavily loaded train and a firebox crammed to the roof with fuel the steam will soon rise to the blowing-off point.

A regulating device could be employed incorporating a Bourdon pressure-gauge tube. The latter may be removed from a gauge, and has the advantage over a spring-loaded piston device in that there is no possibility of leakage. A Bourdon

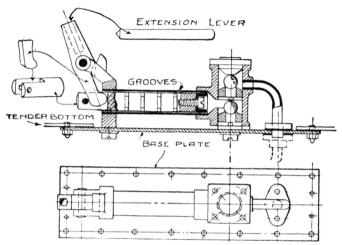

Fig. 349.—Submerged type of hand pump for feed water supply.

tube can be arranged to operate the damper of a closed ashpan fitted under the grate bars, opening the damper when the steam pressure falls and closing it when it rises. As an alternative the Bourdon tube may be made to open a firedoor with an increase in pressure. The fitting of such devices involves calibration and setting of the various parts.

The door must, however, be loose, so that it can be opened independently for purposes of firing. This last-described device is perhaps the simpler and likely to prove the most reliable.

The great advantage of solid firing is the control obtained over the steam evaporation with an engine at rest. So long as the boiler is full of water and the fire replenished even a small model may be left in steam for half an hour at a time without fear of damage. Of course, individual models will have their idiosyncrasies, which will require to be known. Once a model locomotive builder possesses a successful solid-fired engine he will never consider any other scheme.

A good method for raising steam for a small model is illustrated in Fig. 347 and if gas is not available spirit may be employed. The boiler is filled with sufficient water for ten minutes' work, the gas being lighted right away. The engine is then placed over a gas jet and the firebox filled with a layer of fuel. When steam is raised in the small boiler and the auxiliary blower commences working, the Bunsen burner under the fire-grate is lighted. By the time the tin boiler is exhausted steam will be raised and the engine's own blower made available for use.

An air compressor unit with receiver is sometimes employed to supply air to the jet in the extension chimney, although for

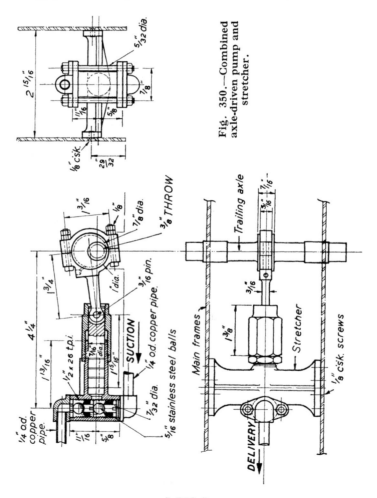

Fig. 350.—Combined axle-driven pump and stretcher.

9½ - in. and 15 - in. gauge engines a 15 ft. extension, of stove-piping, will provide an adequate natural draught. The draught can be started by lighting a fire of paraffined shavings in the smokebox. Then light the usual wood fire in the firebox, using coal when the steam has risen to 10 lb. or 20 lb. per sq. in.

A mixture of anthracite "peas" and good house coal is to be recommended for 1-in. scale and larger engines, while the largest models work well with a mixture of coke and steam coal.

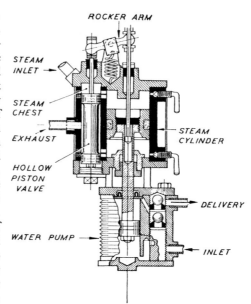

Fig. 350a.—Model vertical double-acting steam-pump.

In designing the cab and tender of a solid-fuel engine convenience in firing should be studied. Sometimes it is necessary to cut a large piece out of the cab and to fit a sliding or lifting roof. The front coal plate of the tender will often be found in the way of the miniature shovel, and should be arranged to be hinged or entirely removable. In a small model tank engine with a closed cab it may pay to fit an inclined chute to the fire-hole with the door in the back bunker. The firehole should in such a case be as high as possible, so that the furnace may be entirely filled with fuel. The chute should be straight, so that poking the fuel into the firebox presents no difficulty. Specially-made firing tools should be devised and made to suit the particular engine. Passenger-carrying tank-engine models are usually fired from a following truck.

Firegrates

Engines burning solid fuel should be provided with a suitable

[293]

grate made up of bars of oblong section placed at a distance apart not greater than their thickness. To preserve these air spaces distance pieces may be employed, as in Fig. 348. Strips of metal, one at each end of the firebox, fixed by studs to the foundation ring, will support a built-up grate. The same applies to the ashpan.

Sometimes it is possible to arrange the grate so that by withdrawing a single pin the grate may be dropped. The whole fire may then be dropped instantly in case of a dangerous shortness of water occurring in the boiler, due to the feed supply failing.

In all solid-fuel engines burning coal, either wholly or partly, the brick arch should never be omitted. This useful fitting prevents the direct passage of cold air to the tubes, and by turning over the flames tends to the more perfect combustion of the fuel. The brick arch may be a piece of refractory tile in a large engine or a thick steel plate. The arch should only rest on special studs and be made free to expand.

Fusible plugs are useful fittings in the furnace to prevent damage to the crown of a boiler. They can be made by soldering in a brass rivet which fits loosely in a hole in a taper-threaded brass plug screwed into the top plate of the firebox (Fig. 352).

Firegrates in $1\frac{3}{4}$-in. and $2\frac{1}{2}$-in. gauge engines may be made from $\frac{3}{32}$-in. or $\frac{1}{8}$-in. round bars. The bars should be shouldered at the ends and riveted into metal strips, after the fashion of a metal ladder, but with close "rungs." The bars should not be too long, and in some cases may run across the width of the firebox rather than lengthwise. Where grates cannot be got into place very easily it may pay to divide the bars into two sets. Engines larger than $1\frac{1}{2}$-in. scale, burning coal and coke, should always be provided with separate cast-iron firebars of the orthodox type.

Hand Pumps

Pumps are varied in type, but the most successful are those having large valves arranged below the normal water level, i.e. "drowned" pumps (Fig. 349). Where pumps are not submerged and have to lift their supply, double (reversed) leathers will be necessary. Ball valves on renewable knife-edged seats are provided. The valves are large and must be made

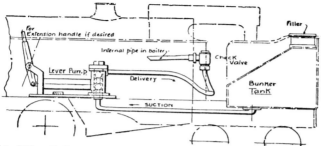

Fig. 351.—Submerged hand pump in side tank of locomotive.

of bronze or stainless steel. The seatings are screwed in, screw-driver slots being provided on their underfaces, the lift being restricted.

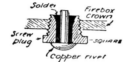

Fig. 352.—D e t a i l of
fusible plug for small
model boiler.

The plunger pump is used on small engines, the lever pump being recommended for larger models. The pump illustrated is fixed on a bedplate, which is studded on to the open bottom plate of the tender tank to provide for its easy removal. The

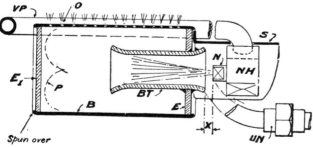

Fig. 353.—Diagram of paraffin burner for small model boiler.
(B) Vaporizing chamber. (P) Baffles. (VP) Vaporizing pipe. (N)
Jet Nozzle.

lever has a loose extension made of round rod, and this projects through a slot in the top of the tank. The lever type of pump may be as large as the tender will accommodate, the limit to the plunger type being about ⅜ in. bore, ⅞ in. being a normally large size. The inside and outside delivery pipes are shown with a flanged connection.

Axle-driven and Steam Pumps

Axle-driven force pumps on locomotives require careful attention. If fitted, some means of ensuring their starting, usually a pet cock on the delivery pipe, must be provided. While this works quite well, it may easily be forgotten by the driver.

An engine which is large enough for an injector may have a hand force pump fitted as a stand-by, but large models should be provided with two injectors, both being maintained in working order.

Where the rear bunker of a tank engine is employed for liquid fuel only the pump may be placed in one of the side tanks. These may be proper water-carrying tanks cross-connected by a suitable balance pipe. Where it is not thought worth while to make the side tanks hold water the pump may be simply hidden by the tank and connected as illustrated in Fig. 351.

The author's design of a vertical double-acting steam-driven pump for ¾-in and 1-in. scale models is shown in Fig. 350a. Its action is entirely automatic; an extension of the piston rod directly operates the piston valve through a spring-loaded rocker lever on the cylinder head.

Injectors

When ¾-in. scale is reached the use of an injector should certainly be considered. Its success is, however, conditional on—

(a) Pipes of ample bore being used.

(b) A check valve which has a passage through it of greater area than the pipes and also a means of shutting it off from the boiler.

(c) The fixing of the injector below the lowest water level of the tank, so that water will flow through the injector by gravity feed.

[296]

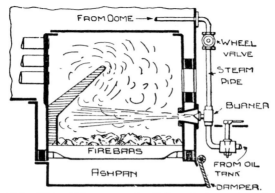

Fig. 354.—Diagram of oil-burning system in firebox.

(d) A water-cock of full bore with a handle convenient to the driver for adjustment purposes (rule for adjustment is low steam pressure, less water, more steam, and vice versa for high steam pressure).

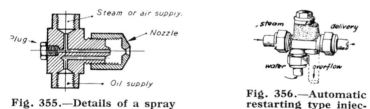

Fig. 355.—Details of a spray burner.

Fig. 356.—Automatic restarting type injector.

(e) Dry steam supply with screw-down valve.
(f) Efficient connections between engine and tender. An air leakage here will certainly cause the injector to fail.

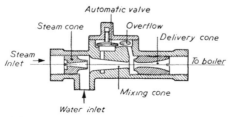

Fig. 356a.—Elements of an injector.

(g) Removable connections to tender to allow tank to be cleaned out periodically.

The injector shown by Fig. 356 is of the automatic restarting type. This type has a valve which releases any pressure accumulating in the combining cone, a state of vacuum being necessary here. The pressure of the fluids is converted into velocity at this point.

Any fur deposit on the cones must be carefully removed preferably in an 8% solution of hydrochloric acid. To operate the injector the water supply is first of all turned on followed by the steam supply. Water will flow through the overflow in the initial stages. By careful regulation of the steam valve, waste water should be reduced to a minimum.

Injectors for models are designed to work from 50 to 100 lb. sq. in. pressure. A small size suitable for $\frac{3}{4}$-in. scale model locomotives will deliver about $1\frac{1}{4}$ pints of water to the boiler per minute. The next size, suitable for $7\frac{1}{4}$-in. gauge models will deliver $1\frac{1}{2}$ to 2 pints per minute. Feed water to an injector should not be at too high a temperature.

Fuel Oil Firing

In 1885 one of Stroudley's tank engines was converted for oil burning. Numerous locomotives in America were also converted about this time. The fundamental principle of oil firing is the thorough atomising of the fuel. This can be accomplished by various systems employing either steam from the boiler or air on mechanical pressure jets. The oil must be broken down into minute particles and mixed with a predetermined quantity of combustible gases and ignited. The fuel oil must burn in suspension with a fairly long flame but avoiding contact with the sides of the firebox. Steam operated burners can be fitted to a moderate size model locomotive provided sufficient firebox volume is available. The quantity of steam required to operate burners is about $\frac{1}{25}$ of the normal steaming capacity of the boiler. It is important to note that solid fuel requires about 50% "excess air" to effect combustion and a fuel oil requires from 25 to 30% "excess air" or say 250 cubic ft. per pound of fuel. Usually a noisy burner is an indication that too much air is being consumed.

A special type of burner for small models is illustrated in

Fig. 353. The reservoir in the tender must be a strong air-tight drum fitted with a filler, air release valve and non-return valve with a connection for an air pump. The diagram Fig. 354 shows an arrangement of a steam-oil spray burner in the firebox of a model which injects oil over the surface of a coal fire. The firebox plates should be protected from the direct action of the jet, particularly in the larger installations. For a small model this method of firing offers few, if any, advantages compensating for the extra fittings it entails. A detail of the burner is shown in Fig. 355. The nozzle is adjusted until the burner delivers a fine clear spray. A strainer for filtering the oil should be located in the pipe line from the reservoir. The oil supply can be pre-heated to advantage to 150° F.

The 15 in. gauge American "Hudson" locomotive built by the Sandley Light Railway Works, Janesville, Wisconsin, U.S.A. is of the oil fired type fitted with an 8-in. diameter firing tube. The boiler is a Scotch Marine return-tube type and works at a pressure of 200 lb. sq. in. (Fig. 3).

The presence of smoke indicates insufficient air supply to the firebox. The oil pressure may be too low or not hot enough. Too much air will lower the temperature of the firebox.

To light the burners, the ignition flame must be applied *before* the oil supply is turned on. Care must be taken to prevent a burner from being extinguished while the engine is working as an explosive mixture of vapour will be drawn through the tubes and smokebox. The maintenance of the burners is very important.

CHAPTER XVI

BRAKE SYSTEMS

SPECIAL attention must be given to the design of brake gear for a model locomotive employed for passenger hauling purposes. The complete train when running at speed has stored up kinetic energy including the rotational energy of all the wheels which behave in the same way as flywheels on stationary engines. The action of the brakes is to destroy this energy and bring the train to rest. The rate of retardation will be of the order of 3 or 4 ft. per second/per second (or about –0.lg). Thus a large miniature railway train travelling at 15 m.p.h. on a level track would be brought to rest in 25 yds. Since the kinetic energy varies as the square of the speed, the same train travelling at 30 m.p.h. would require about 100 yds. to come to rest.

The arrangement of rigging brake blocks will depend on design. For small models it is not usual to introduce complicated compensating levers. If the brakes are much used the amount of wear and tear on the blocks and pins soon puts the relatively short levers out of gear. Blocks should be strongly hung from the main frames (see Fig. 325), and the cross rods tying the brake hangers together should be flat beams with the ends turned to form pins. The forked ends of the rods should be pinned to the beams. For small passenger-carrying models power brakes are practicable on the engine wheels, but as the main weight is behind the engine the retarding effect of the most powerful brake is small owing to the low percentage of weight which is braked. On tender engines from $7\frac{1}{4}$ in. to 15 in. gauge a satisfactory arrangement is a foot brake on the tender with a power brake on the engine.

Steam Brake System

The locomotive brakes are operated by a steam cylinder (Fig. 365) located at a convenient point between the frames— usually below the cab footplate. Steam to the cylinder is taken from the boiler at full pressure and regulated by a driver's valve fitted in the cab.

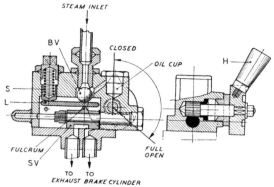

Fig. 357.—Greenly's variable pressure steam brake
valve.

The diagram Fig. 357 shows an arrangement of variable
pressure brake valve. In this system the slide valve sv, as drawn,
is shut off to live steam and the supply to the brake cylinder is
open to the exhaust pipe and atmosphere. The spring s on the
lever L maintains the ball valve BV in the closed position and
steam is cut off. By operating the handle H the port to the
cylinder feed pipe is opened. At the same time the fulcrum
of the lever L which is part of the slide valve, is moved so that
the leverage changes in favour of the steam supply and the ball
valve is forced open. Thus the pressure on the brake cylinder
and brakes varies according to the position of the hand-controlled
slide valve since the pressure due to the spring regulates the
quantity of steam admitted.

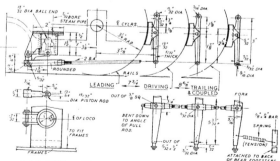

Fig. 358.—Non-compensated brake system.

[301]

An advantage of a steam brake system over air or vacuum schemes is that pressure is always available from the boiler. The power transmitted to a distant brake system along the train can, however, be lost due to condensation in the steam pipes.

The action of the steam brake when first applied is sluggish. On warming up the pressure builds up and, as speed is reduced, the intensity of pressure on the wheels is increased. The pressure on the brake blocks cannot be regulated by an ordinary steam stop valve. The retarding pressure should be reduced with the deceleration of the train. At high speeds a greater force can be applied whereas at comparatively slower speeds, less pressure is required.

Vacuum Brake Systems

Primarily, the vacuum brake is controlled by the pressure of the atmosphere on one side of a piston in the operating cylinder. The other side of the piston is maintained at a pressure below atmospheric for the purpose of either keeping the brakes "on" or "off" according to the system adopted. The reduced pressure may vary between 12 in. to 25 in. of vacuum or 9 to 2·4 lb. sq. in. absolute. Thus the effective pressure on the piston is the difference between atmospheric and the reduced pressures. At sea level, for a 20-in. vacuum, the difference is: $14·7 - 5 = 9·7$ lb. sq. in. A high vacuum is desirable to obtain the best results.

A useful power brake system that can be employed for the smaller passenger-carrying locomotive is the "simple" vacuum brake. A combined ejector and driver's valve operated by a single handle is fitted in the cab. The apparatus comprises a cam-operated valve regulating the steam supply to the ejector, a non-return valve, air inlet valve and connections for the steam supply, train pipe and drain (Fig. 359).

There are three main positions of the handle: (1) The steam valve is opened by the cam and steam admitted to the nozzle and cones. Air is evacuated from the train-pipe system and a reduced pressure maintained. (2) The steam valve is closed and the vacuum held in the train pipe. The check valve is kept closed by external atmospheric pressure. (3) The steam valve is kept closed but free air is admitted to the train pipe and the vacuum in the system is destroyed.

[302]

In the "simple" system to stop the train the driver's handle is placed in position (1). The brakes are applied. In position (2) the brakes are held "on" and for (3) they are released.

Automatic Vacuum Brake

In the automatic system the vacuum is maintained in the train pipe during the period when the train is in motion. When air is admitted to the train pipe, via the driver's valve, the

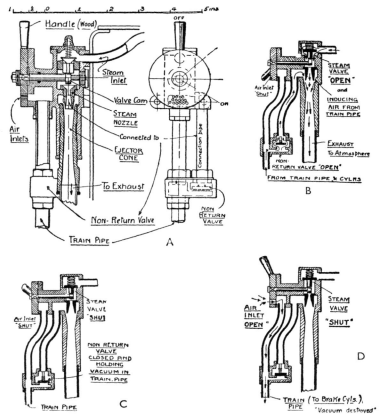

Fig. 359.—Greenly's vacuum brake ejector and driver's valve. (A) Diagram showing various parts. (B) Non-return valve open. (C) Non-return valve closed. Vacuum held. (D) Steam valve shut and Air inlet open.

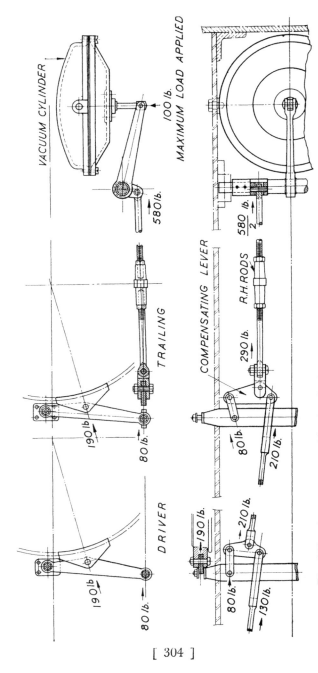

VACUUM CYLINDER

MAXIMUM LOAD APPLIED

100 lb.

580 lb.

580 lb.
2

TRAILING

DRIVER

190 lb

80 lb.

190 lb

80 lb.

COMPENSATING LEVER

R.H. RODS

290 lb.

80 lb.

210 lb.

190 lb.

210 lb.

80 lb.

130 lb.

Fig. 360.—Arrangement of brake rigging with compensating gear for 7¼-in. gauge locomotive.

[304]

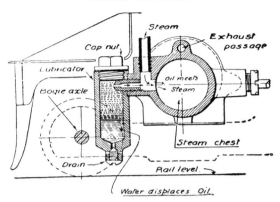

**Fig. 361.—Arrangement of Roscoe displacement
lubricator.**

balance of pressure in the brake cylinder is disturbed, and the
brakes are instantly applied. In order to maintain the necessary
degree of vacuum, a small secondary ejector is fitted to the
combined driver's valve and ejector. For the small model locomotive the scheme is not recommended as it can be very wasteful
of steam.

Fig. 364 shows the type of vacuum brake cylinder designed
for 1-in. scale models. The piston is in the form of a sealed
diaphragm dividing the cylinder into two chambers: one
exposed to atmospheric pressure and the other connected to the
vacuum system.

It is important to note that the maximum pressure exerted
by a diaphragm type of cylinder is not equal to that of an

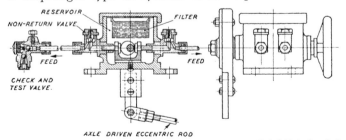

(*Courtesy. Messrs C. C. Wakefield & Co., Ltd.*)

**Fig. 362.—Wakefield four-feed model mechanical lubricator
designed for 1½-in. scale locomotives.**

U

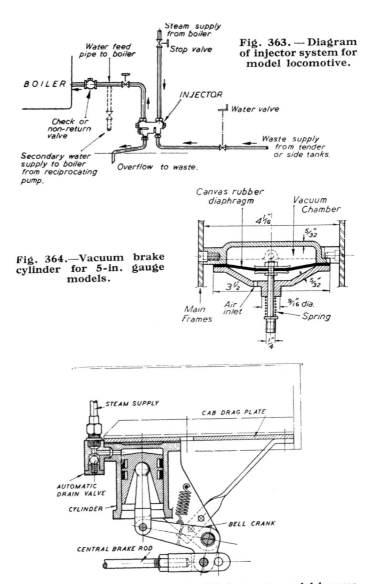

Fig. 363. — Diagram of injector system for model locomotive.

Steam supply from boiler

Water feed pipe to boiler

Stop valve

BOILER

INJECTOR

Water valve

Check or non-return valve

Secondary water supply to boiler from reciprocating pump.

Overflow to waste.

Waste supply from tender or side tanks.

Fig. 364.—Vacuum brake cylinder for 5-in. gauge models.

Canvas rubber diaphragm

Vacuum Chamber

$4\frac{1}{16}''$

$\frac{5}{32}''$

$3\frac{1}{2}$

$\frac{5}{32}''$

Main Frames

Air inlet

$\frac{9}{16}''$ dia.

Spring

$\frac{1}{4}''$

STEAM SUPPLY

CAB DRAG PLATE

AUTOMATIC DRAIN VALVE

CYLINDER

BELL CRANK

CENTRAL BRAKE ROD

Fig. 365.—Steam brake cylinder for $10\frac{1}{4}$-in gauge model locomotive. (The automatic valve remains shut under steam pressure, but when steam is shut off, condensation creates a vacuum in the system and the atmospheric pressure opens the valve.)

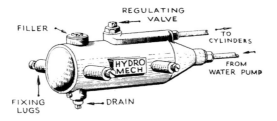

Fig. 366.—Displacement type lubricator. Oil is forced into the steampipe by pressure of water from pump.

(Photo: Bassett-Lowke Ltd.)

Fig. 367.—Greenly's vacuum brake ejector and driver's valve for 2-in. scale model.

ordinary piston sliding in a cylinder of the same dimensions, but can only be a fraction of the latter (about $\frac{2}{3}$).

Model Locomotive Research

In full size practice the testing stand for a locomotive is designed to measure tractive effort at various speeds by means of a dynamometer. The actual work done at the tread of the coupled wheels can therefore be accurately determined. In conjunction with these power tests, the boiler is also tested for fuel and water consumption. The British Railways Testing Station at Rugby, which was opened in October 1948, is fully equipped with all the plant and instruments for testing full-size locomotives.

For testing small models a special frame fitted with rails for the carrying wheels and rollers for the coupled wheels is a useful workshop fixture. The rollers are free to rotate with the coupled wheels and thus form an endless track upon which the locomotive can be "run". The spring is anchored at one end—preferably to a fixed spring balance or other recording device for measuring draw-bar pull.

With free running rollers the locomotive can be regarded as travelling "light," having only frictional resistance to overcome. Under these conditions the regulator must be throttled in conjunction with an early cut-off otherwise the engine will race to a critical, if not dangerous, speed.

Resistance to turning of the coupled wheels, equivalent to the loads the engine has to haul, is provided for by braking on the rollers. The throttle is opened to give the additional power required to overcome resistance and to maintain speed. It will be noted that the hitherto free exhaust from the blast pipe is sharpened to the well-known heavy beat of an engine under load. The firebox draught is also automatically increased under these conditions of driving.

The brake acting on the rollers can be fitted up as a dynamometer whereby the actual loads on the wheel treads can be accurately measured under varying conditions from starting to full speed. In its simplest form, the brake or dynamometer can be replaced by a flywheel fitted to each of the roller axles.

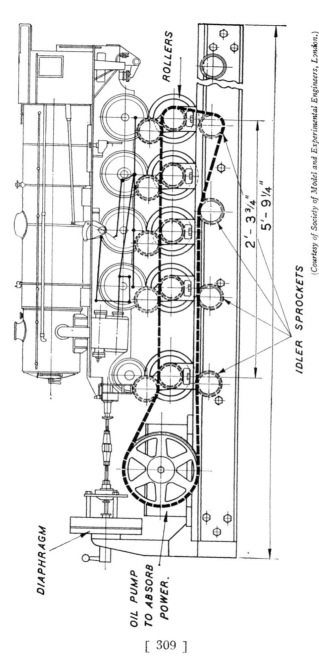

ROLLERS

IDLER SPROCKETS

2'- 3¾"

5'- 9¼"

DIAPHRAGM

OIL PUMP
TO ABSORB
POWER.

(*Courtesy of Society of Model and Experimental Engineers, London.*)

Fig. 368.—Diagram of the S.M.E.E. test bench with model locomotive in position.

The S.M.E.E. Test Bench

Members of the Society of Model and Experimental Engineers have evolved a miniature locomotive test bench which was completed and shown working at the Society's Jubilee Exhibition in 1948 and at subsequent "Model Engineer" exhibitions in London.

The diagrams (Fig. 368) show the general arrangement of the apparatus with a locomotive in position for testing. The front end of the locomotive is shown coupled direct to the diaphragm and the draw-bar pull is measured on a liquid manometer connected to it. The power developed by the locomotive is absorbed by the high-pressure pump through the chain drive. A 5-in. gauge model of the "Princess Royal" tested on the bench developed 2 h.p. at a speed of 15 m.p.h. (Tractive

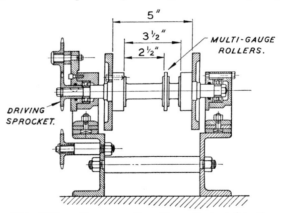

Fig. 368a.—Cross-section through test bench.

effort: 75 lb.) In conjunction with these tests, the distance travelled, fuel and water consumption, smokebox vacuum and superheat temperatures were recorded.

Lubrication Systems

Oil administered at the right moment to valves and pistons make a considerable difference in the running of an engine. A good lubricating arrangement in thorough working order will produce the same freedom of working in a model which is mechanically efficient. Mechanical or some form of hydrostatic or displacement type of lubricator can be employed. Grease gun of the screw-down type can, if necessary, be adopted and has proved quite satisfactory in practice.

Fig. 362 shows the standard Wakefield model mechanical lubricator which can be fitted to 7¼-in. gauge model locomotives. The lubricator is designed for either two or four feeds to the respective cylinders. Check and oil test valves are also fitted.

With a mechanical system of lubrication a positive pressure can be maintained which is independent of the steam supply. The quantity of oil that is fed to the cylinder is approximately proportional to the speed of the engine.

The "Roscoe" type displacement lubricator (Fig. 361) should be located in a cool position and where the filler cap is also accessible. For large models a needle valve is fitted to regulate the flow of oil. Steam admitted to the oil reservoir displaces and vaporizes the oil which is then forced into the cylinder steam chest. Eventually all oil in the reservoir is displaced by condensed steam which must be drained off and the lubricator recharged with oil.

In the hydrostatic type of lubricator (Fig. 366) water pressure from the feed pump forces the oil through a needle control valve to the steam chest.

For a small model oil from a reservoir can be forced by compressed air along feed pipes to the valve chests. Air is supplied from a hand pump and the supply of oil regulated by a suitable needle valve. By pumping the oil to a pressure in excess of steam chest pressure continuity of flow is obtained. An air pressure gauge is connected to the reservoir. The reservoir should be of sufficient capacity so that the maximum quantity of oil required should fill it by no more than a third. Provision can also be made for a slight feed complete with valve, check valve and water release cock.

Bearings and all rubbing surfaces must be suitably lubricated to ensure smooth running of the locomotive. The methods adopted may range from the simple oil hole for a small model to a more comprehensive remote-control system employed in a large-gauge engine. But whatever system is adopted, it is of fundamental importance to see that care and maintenance of the various working parts receive periodic attention. Where ball and roller bearings are fitted to any part of an engine, the advice and recommendations of the manufacturers should be followed.

[311]

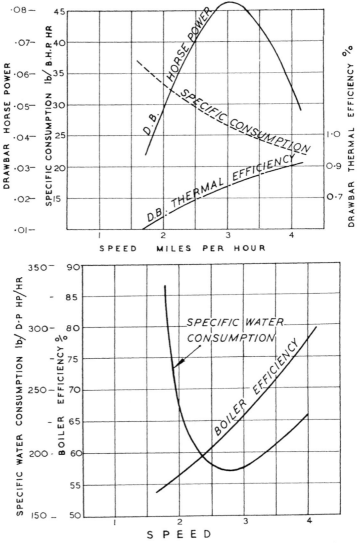

Fig. 369.—Charts showing results of tests on the S.M.E.E. locomotive test stand for a 0–6–0 locomotive.

(1) Draw-bar horsepower.
(2) Specific consumption (fuel).
(3) Thermal efficiency.
(4) Specific water consumption.
(5) Boiler efficiency.

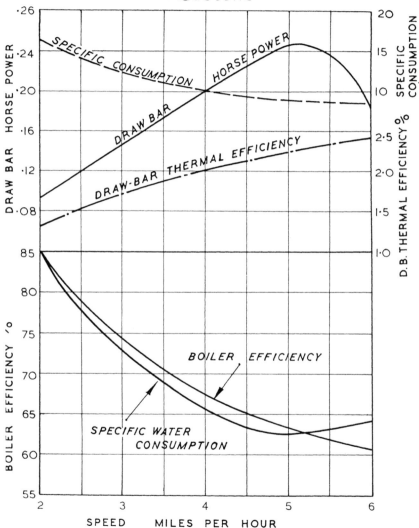

Fig. 370.—Results of tests on a model 0-4-2 locomotive.

[313]

TABLE XIV

15-in. GAUGE LOCOMOTIVES

(Designed by Henry Greenly)

Name	Railway	Builder	Type	Date
Little Giant	Blackpool	Bassett-Lowke	4–4–2	1905
Sans Pareil	Ravenglass	Bassett-Lowke	4–4–2	1911
Colossus	Staughton Manor	Bassett-Lowke	4–6–2	1915
Green Goddess	R. H. and D.	Davey Paxman	4–6–2	1925
Northern Chief	,,	,,	4–6–2	1925
Southern Maid	,,	,,	4–6–2	1927
Hercules	,,	,,	4–8–2	1927
Samson	,,	,,	4–8–2	1927
Typhoon	,,	,,	4–6–2	1927
Hurricane	,,	,,	4–6–2	1927

THE Author is indebted to Mr. G. W. Wildy, Chairman of the Stationary Engine Committee of the Society of Model and Experimental Engineers for the assistance he has rendered in supplying particulars of the test bench described in this chapter and for his permission to use the charts shown in Figs. 369 and 370. The test on the 0–6–0 locomotive shows the draw-bar horsepower at speeds up to 4 m.p.h. It will be observed that, when the speed is increased beyond 3 m.p.h., there is a decrease in the power output at the draw-bar. This is due to the power being absorbed by the machinery itself, so that at 5 m.p.h. or thereabouts, nearly all the available power would have been absorbed, with nothing left for the draw-bar.

For the model locomotive "Gladstone" (0–4–2) the draw-bar pull rapidly decreases when accelerated above $6\frac{1}{2}$ m.p.h. Other characteristics of these curves are the increased thermal efficiencies with a corresponding decrease in fuel consumption at the higher speeds. The water consumption is also at a minimum for maximum draw-bar pull.

INDEX